C2 000002 139835 06

D0496758

Are You Looking At Me, Jimmy ?

Arnold Brown

Are You Looking At Me, Jimmy ?

Mysteries of a great city

with drawings by Ken Cox

Methuen

First published in Great Britain in 1994
by Methuen London
an imprint of Reed Consumer Books Ltd
Michelin House, 81 Fulham Road, London SW3 6RB
and Auckland, Melbourne, Singapore and Toronto
Reprinted 1994

Copyright © 1994 by Arnold Brown
Drawings copyright © 1994 by Ken Cox
The author and artist have asserted their moral rights

A CIP catalogue record for this title
is available from the British Library
ISBN 0 413 68890 9

Typeset by Falcon Graphic Art Ltd
Wallington, Surrey
Printed in Great Britain
by Clays Ltd, St Ives PLC

This book is sold subject to the condition
that it shall not, by way of trade or otherwise,
be lent, resold, hired out, or otherwise circulated
without the publisher's prior consent in any form
of binding or cover other than that in which
it is published and without a similar condition
including this condition being imposed
on the subsequent purchaser.

To Liz

Thanks to Geoffrey Strachan, Liz Kneen,
Ken Ellis and Jerry Hicks.

Contents

Prologue

See me, Jimmy. I'm from Glasgow. That's where the big ships like the *Queen Elizabeth* and the *Queen Mary* used to be coaxed into the Clyde at the nudge of a champagne bottle. Ships as big as tenements, Jimmy.

10   Shipbuilding. An intricate pastime, Jimmy. There's a million and one details to chew over before a man-made leviathan can slide into the sea to join the other creatures doon the watter. For a start, you need unlimited supplies of steel and hot-blast furnaces that blaze up the sky. Tenders that leave your rivals gasping. A world economy with a smile on its face. But the party's over, my riveter friend. Not only on Clydeside.

It's also all not happening in places like Merseyside and Tyneside. It's obvious that whenever great industrial ports are on the skids, the populace need cheering up. You gotta laugh, Jimmy.

That's why nowadays, the strange fact is that Comedy Festivals are springing up in the shipbuilding wastelands. Glasgow, Liverpool, Newcastle . . . A few performers, a stage, a mike, an audience, a bar at the back . . . Not difficult to launch.

'And may God bless all who laugh, giggle and titter in her.'

I'm just back from the Newcastle Comedy Festival. I used to be a sit-down accountant, but since the recession you've got to go where the work is . . . So now I'm a stand-up comedian.

Don't give me all that heavy-duty stuff about there being no more than seven or eight basic jokes since the creation of the universe. That's the kind of rumour that makes the comedy fraternity top themselves in lonely motels in the Australian outback or, even worse, rush to appear in *Celebrity Squares* on TV.

I've got to admit that before any performance, there's always that mixture of adrenalin and fear, an awareness you could suddenly topple into the Silence Vortex. The black hole from which few comedians ever return.

If it's that dicey, why bother? I hear you ask.

Well, we're trying to get the attention we never got as adults.

That's *my* theory.

'ARE YOU LOOKING AT ME, JIMMY?'

I hope so.

1   Newsflash!

I'm on my way home back to Hampstead, London NW3. As I come out of the Underground, outside McDonald's I notice a lone tiny figure in an anorak. This is his third month of protest. It's a silent vigil. He holds his placard high up in the air, as if it's a religious cross, and to him it probably is: 'SMALL VEGANS SAY NO TO BIG MACS'.

Outside Oddbins off-licence, two low-alcohol lager louts argue politely with each other. 'I think it's *your* turn to hit him, Tristan . . .' 'No, no, Peregrine, you're definitely wrong. It's *your* turn.'

Outside Waterstone's bookshop, tanks and troops with Kalashnikovs are everywhere. Inside, Jeffrey Archer prepares for his first public book-signing since the *fatwah*.

I'm back in my flat. It's small but uncomfortable. The answering machine flashes at me.

'Hello, hen. This is your Auntie Sophie. I interrupt your life with a newsflash. Uncle Harry is dead.'

I was stunned, although of course when someone's ninety-nine years old, you don't buy them Five Year diaries any more. The bleak message continued . . .

'Late last night at 51 Calder Street, Crosshill, Glasgow, Harry Brown passed away. The funeral is to be held at Glenduffhill Cemetery this coming Friday at 3 p.m. No Sony Walkmans, portable phones or lap-tops by request. What dae you think of that newsflash, Arnold? Just like they dae it on the telly news, eh? Ah could have been a news announcer, nae bother . . . But it's all these anti-Semites – they're dead prejudiced against ninety-year-old Jews. And being a woman disnae help either. Oh, hen, ah nearly forgot. Ring Solomon and Solomon, Solicitors. 041 330 2121. Harry left you everything, including the rocking-horse. My brother was a bit of a *meshuggener*, and we never saw eye to eye, but everyone respected him. He was a *mensh*.'

She was crying. 'Oh, one last thing, hen. At the end, Harry mentioned an instruction he got from that angel of his. You know, David. The rabbi's got to conduct the entire Kaddish on stilts. Bye, hen. See you at – .'

The tape had run out.

Just like Harry's life.

As for the funeral service on stilts, angels, and of course, that business Harry told me months ago about his shadow getting smaller and smaller, the sign of impending death, it was all to do with Harry's obsession with the Kabbalah, the Jewish mystical movement that started in Europe in the thirteenth century. Take that tram story. Over the years I had started to tape-record Harry's reminiscences at his flat.

14   'I remember, Arnold, it was some time in 1947 around the Fair Fortnight. I was going up to the Queen's Park to have a blether with my pals. We all used to meet on the benches at the top of the hill overlooking the bandstand.

I like seeing panoramic views and people enjoying themselves. I was on top of the tram coming down Eglinton Toll into Victoria Road and I was deep in thought. You know how it is, Arnold.

'I was thinking how good life was now that the war was over, even though of course, times were still hard. Rationing, coupons, all that. I was thinking: surely there must be a way to avoid wars in future. What was the solution? How can society achieve permanent peace? As I was chewing over these questions, a big *yock* in overalls sat down on the seat right next to me. And that's when it started. You know, each of us shuffling our bums around, jockeying for positions, trying to keep as much space as possible to ourselves. Then it suddenly struck me. Space.

That's what all the trouble in the world's about. Too many bums chasing too few seats. I pondered the problem for a few minutes and it suddenly dawned on me. Surely the answer was to get all the businesses and organisations in the country to pair up with each other. Save rent, save space. For example, there was a baked-potato take-away opening round the corner from me in Allison Street. Nearby was the Buddhist centre where I used to go to meditate three times a week. Surely the obvious thing to do was to combine the two premises and run them under the one roof: maybe they could call it "The Spud-u-Like Meditation Centre". I noted the idea down in my "Inspirations" notebook, which I carried with me at all times.

'Suddenly I had the top deck of the tram all to myself and I was stretching my legs. Then, even though it was a warm summer day, I felt a sudden chill. I heard this scuffling movement behind me. At first I thought it was the ticket inspector. But whoever I saw in front of me was no employee of Glasgow Corporation, that was for sure. It was this tall gentleman with a black beard flecked with white. He was dressed in a radiant white gown. He had a kind face and was smiling. Then I realised to my amazement that he wasn't standing on the floor of the tram. Oh no. He was actually *floating* a few inches above it.

'Now you would have thought I'd be quaking in my boots. Strange thing is, Arnold, I didn't feel in the least scared. In fact, I was feeling a warm glow of happiness. I had never experienced such a mystical presence before, but I somehow knew that the right thing to do was to let him speak first. And he did, in a soft yet powerful voice. "Harry. Hello. Going to the Queen's Park for a gossip with the *yachnes*? I thought I'd catch you before you got there."

'I realised he was a Yiddishe man like myself.

'The stranger continued: "My name's David. I've been appointed as your angel. It's official. On a first meeting like this, we never get embroiled in anything too involved or the really big issues. We just start with a few basic tips. Here they are:

> *One.*   Never sleep' in a field of buttercups in the week before the Day of Atonement. That tempts the evil spirits.

> *Two.*   Always say a blessing each night for your eyebrows. People take eyebrows for granted. *Don't.* And finally –

> *Three.*   Put a quid each way on Scotia Lad in the 3.30 at Ayr tomorrow. It's fifty to one. I have inside information. It'll be like taking sweeties from a baby.

"OK, Harry. Better go before a ticket inspector pops up. Goodbye. Oh yes, and one last thing – a little gift." He then pressed something into my hand and vanished.

'I looked down astounded. It was an orange.'

2 Situation Vacant

To understand Uncle Harry, we'll have to go back to Moscow in 1825. Nicholas Romanov, an evil and crazy young man, paused to look in the window of the main Job Centre. His evil and crazy eyes immediately pounced on a small card in the 'Situations Vacant' section:

WANTED IMMEDIATELY.
EVIL MADMAN TO OPPRESS
MILLIONS OF PEASANTS.
APPLY WITHIN.
NO PREVIOUS EXPERIENCE REQUIRED.
NO TIME-WASTERS PLEASE.

He thought to himself – why not? – and walked in.

The Chairman of the Interviewing Committee spoke first. 'Let me explain the particular background of this important position. As you know, Nicholas, the Russian Empire is a big place. So it's not surprising there are many

18 problems. For a start, food. The peasants are very angry because they are . . . how shall I put it??? *Starving*. There. I've said it. Yes, *starving*. And that means revolution and chaos – which, of course, in turn means the end of the luxurious way of life we in the upper classes require for our contentment of mind. How can we avoid this, Nicholas? Quite simply, we need ideas, fresh ideas, and quick.'

Nicholas leaned forward in his chair and with a maniacal glint in his eyes, whispered evilly: 'Scapegoat. Get yourselves a scapegoat.'

'Scapegoat?' the Chairman repeated, puzzled. 'What's that? Explain yourself, please.'

Nicholas smiled his twisted evil smile. 'When anything goes wrong, just blame it on the scapegoat.'

'Sounds perfect. In fact, my dear chap, positively ingenious. But wait. Where can we find such a scapegoat?'

Nicholas chuckled the evil chuckle which he practised daily. 'There's no need to look very far. You've got a scapegoat staring you in the face. The Chosen People. The Jews.'

The whole committee laughed delightedly. 'Of course, you're right; the Jews. Why didn't we think of this before? It's so obvious – and so simple.'

'When do I start?' asked Nicholas.

'Right away.'

'OK. Here's plan number one, gentlemen. Tomorrow we spread the rumour that the Jews are poisoning the wells.'

'Love it,' said the Chairman. 'Glad to have you on board, Nicholas.'

And so Nicholas became Czar of all the Russias and the czars continued to reign, passing their franchise of evil from father to son for the rest of the century.

3   The shtetl

In 1899, hundreds of thousands of Jews were living in Lithuania, part of the Russian Empire. Who would have predicted that only one year later in 1900, some of these very same Jews would find themselves in the gallery of Scotland's leading variety theatre, the Glasgow Empire?

Lithuania. Winter 1899
Abraham Lizerbram, a tailor, his wife Sarah and their son Herschel (later Harry), a five-year-old infant prodigy, lived in the *shtetl*, a small town. Here in the Pale of Settlement, the Jews were confined, unable to work or travel without the permission of the authorities. They lived in ramshackle wooden houses and were forbidden to own land. They were barred from universities and from the lowest government jobs. As many trades and crafts were also officially closed to them, the entrepreneurial Jew evolved, specialising in occupations that could be set up without any outside interference. They became pedlars, tailors, cobblers, butchers, small shopkeepers, market traders.

Although they were right at the bottom of the heap, the Jews had one significant reason to be optimistic about the future. They had friends in high places. To be more

precise, they had one very influential friend. The Almighty.
From the start, the Jews were always great name-droppers.
'I was speaking to God only last night . . .'

A *broche* is a prayer of thanksgiving to the Lord, and being very *frum* (religious), Abraham said *broches* hundreds of times a day. This habit secretly annoyed his wife and son, but they never let him know this. Some families are like that. One evening, Sarah saw that her husband had that certain pre-*broche* look that she knew so well. She thought to herself: 'Enough is enough. I'll divert Abraham's attention by showing him the letters from my cousin Solomon who sailed to Scotland three months ago.'

'The Retreat'
15 Nithsdale Crescent
Pollokshields
Glasgow
Scotland

16th November 1899

Dear Sarah, Abraham and Herschel
How happy I am to have escaped from the miseries of the *shtetl*. I think of you all every day.
After a very smooth crossing on an ocean liner, I arrived in Glasgow, and after only a few weeks have set up my own tailoring factory employing over one hundred workers. In a short time, I have accumulated enough money to buy a large house in the most elegant part of the city.
Scotland is a wonderful country. The streets are paved with gold. Come as soon as you can.
Shalom,
Cousin Solomon

Sarah then showed Abraham the second letter which, by coincidence, had arrived at the same time as the first one.

11 Portugal Street
The Gorbals
Glasgow
Scotland

23rd November 1899

Dear Sarah, Abraham and Herschel

I have just managed to recover from a terrible accident. I was walking towards Gorbals Cross when an object fell out of the sky and hit me hard on the head.

What had happened was this. A couple on the top storey of a tenement were having an argument and the wife was so angry she threw a haggis at her husband. (The haggis is minced heart, lungs and liver of a sheep. The people here boil it in a bag with oatmeal.) Anyway, the husband must have ducked, for the haggis flew right out the open window into the street below and knocked me unconscious. After that, I lost my memory for a time. I can't remember if I sent you a letter or not. I've been a bit confused, so if I did, just ignore it. Life is hard in Scotland, but I managed to get a job as a tailor's presser in a small factory in the Gorbals. It's a living. I've got a little room in a tenement here in Portugal Street, which I share with two other workers from the factory. There's lots of other Yidden here, and the toilet and wash-hand basin are in use from morning to night. In fact, conditions in the tenement are just about as cramped as they were on the boat. But the good news is the Scots leave us in peace. They don't persecute us like those *momzers* in the Old Country.

Try and come to Glasgow soon.

Shalom and och aye the noo,

Cousin Solomon

4   The ship

And so Abraham and Sarah decided to leave Lithuania and sail for Scotland with Herschel. One week before the family departed, Abraham decided it was time to have a serious talk with his son.

'Herschel, I have to tell you one important fact. We Jews are the Chosen People.'

'Chosen for what, Father?'

'To ask questions, my dear Herschel.'

'Is it good to ask questions, Father?'

'Yes, Herschel, the Almighty has put us on this earth to do this.'

'Father, are there answers to all these questions?'

'Ah,' said Abraham. 'That's exactly the point. The Jewish contribution to civilisation is to *try* to find answers to all these questions. Questions like . . . Why are we here? Where are we going? Who is going with us? Are we coming back? And above all: Shall we be taking sandwiches?'

Herschel thought for a few seconds. 'What kind of sandwiches, Father?'

'What an important question, Herschel. You're learning already.'

At one end of the quayside on the morning of their departure, Abraham, Sarah and Herschel joined the long queue for the boat going to Scotland. At the other end of the quay, auditions were being conducted for families who were sailing for New York. Singers, musicians, dancers. All came under the scrutiny of cigar-chewing Broadway producers and agents who were looking for fresh talent with which to wow the New World.

On the seventh day of the voyage, Abraham won the first prize (a crust of bread and one pickled herring) in the ship's weekly competition for the most imaginative curse on the Czar: 'May his nose run continuously and his hands be so stiff, he is unable to wipe it for eternity.'

At sunrise on the sixteenth day of the voyage, there were excited shouts from all the passengers. One seagull flying overhead was very different from the others. On its head was a tiny skull cap and floating between its wings was an equally tiny prayer shawl. Everyone on board began to pray and the congregation recited to the heavens.

'SHMAH YISRAEL, Hear O Israel.'

The Scots have the custom of seeing in the New Year by greeting the 'first-foot', who comes over the threshold with traditional gifts, like shortbread and a black bun. Dark-complexioned visitors are particularly welcome. But the bleary-eyed Jews who staggered into Scotland on the stroke of midnight on 31st December, 1899 were completely unaware of all of this.

5   Return to Glasgow

Inter-City train. 10 a.m. London–Glasgow
At Euston Station, hidden security cameras scanned the
scene, searching for terrorists, bombs and buskers. Using
a pre-arranged code word, a man with a thick Irish accent
makes a call to British Rail headquarters.

'. . . and in fifteen minutes precisely, I will be playing
Dylan's "Blowing In The Wind" in one of your stations.
No, I am unable to specify the exact location.' Click –
followed by dialling tone.

Emergency Services rush into action.

As soon as the train moves off, fingers
start jabbing at the portable phones.

'Hello Tristan, I'm just leaving London.'

'I'm on the train, Fiona darling.'

'I'm eating a Mars Bar, Nanny.'

High tech: low intelligence. I've got to admit, though, these message-toys are dead brilliant. After all, I can still remember the excitement when we were the first family in our street in Glasgow to have cordless *pyjamas*. The neighbours were so chuffed they gave a party for us and they all danced around my mother and father.

'How do they keep up?'

'Easy. Will-power.'

A few hours later an uncompromisingly Glasgow voice came crackling over the tannoy: 'Ladies and gentlemen. This is your guard speaking. We are now in Scotland. Please observe two minutes' silence for the Battle of Flodden, the Highland Clearances and Scotland's non-appearance in the 1994 World Cup.' The whole train hushed into reverential silence at this reminder of Scottish grievances, past and present. 'Thank you for that mark of respect,' the guard continued. 'I would now like to recite a poem about one of Scotland's natural assets.

> It's Scottish Water,
> Do not forget it,
> It's *our* water,
> From Scottish lochs and rivers,
> Don't dare touch it,
> Privatise it over my dead body,
> ENGLISH BASTARDS!

Thank you.'

All along the train there was the sound of whooping and cheering.

Eventually we rolled into Glasgow Central Station. Outside the ticket barrier, a man approached me. He'd obviously seen better days.

'Excuse me, Jimmy. Have you any spare compliments? I haven't had a compliment in months.'

I looked at him closely. The man was desperate. It's an uncaring world. No doubt about it. I couldn't turn him away empty-handed. Uncle Harry had taught me compassion. (He once told me he always wore a hat to cover his hair, so as not to embarrass bald people. That's the kind of person Uncle Harry was.)

'You've got a very distinguished Roman nose there,' I said.

'Thanks, son. You've made ma day, so y'have. Thanks a million.' He shuffled off, a happier man.

Outside the station, I walked up the hill to St Vincent Street to the offices of Solomon and Solomon, Solicitors.

It was all obscenely quick and formal. A file marked 'Harry Brown, deceased'. I signed a few documents, received the keys of my uncle's flat at 51 Calder Street and a letter marked 'FOR THE ATTENTION OF MY NEPHEW, ARNOLD BROWN'.

Twenty short minutes later, I was out in the street again. I read the letter.

Dear Arnold
We are all left-luggage waiting to be collected.
Yours affectionately,
Uncle Harry

Thanks very much, Harry. Talk about meaningful insights . . .

6   51 Calder Street

Number 51 Calder Street is in the south side of Glasgow, just off Victoria Road, where Harry met his angel, David, on the tram all those years ago. The tenement flat was on the ground floor and outside, a blue plaque indicated that this had been the residence of no ordinary citizen.

HARRY BROWN
Philosopher & Fruiterer
lived here
1946–1993

The City Fathers had obviously wasted no time in honouring one of their sons.

I turned the key in the door and walked into the front room. The rocking-horse was there, as promised. Strangely, it didn't seem out of place. Some rare souls like Harry manage to conjure up second and even third childhoods. No bother at all. In front of the rocking-horse, there was a small table on which stood a pair of silver candlesticks. Had the feisty old agnostic finally been seduced by the warming embrace of religion? Or on Friday evenings, had

he prayed that there was no God? But who do you pray
to for that?

I tried to picture Harry's last few years in the flat. Old age can be a series of journeys as hazardous as reaching the South Pole. You manage to get from the bedroom to the toilet and you plant your flag successfully at your destination. That's what peeing's all about when you're ninety-nine, Jimmy . . .

On the sideboard there was an old sepia photograph of Grandfather Abraham Lizerbram, standing proudly outside his tailor shop in Crown Street in the Gorbals, circa 1928. Around his neck, the portable tool of his trade, a tape measure. Give me an inch and I'll make you a suit, he always used to say.

I sat down on the wooden chair that looked the least rickety. I have an instinct for these sort of things. A mustiness hung in the air. At first glance, or even second, Harry's flat was no obvious choice for the cover of *Hello* magazine. In the bedroom I confronted an enigma . . .

'EXHIBITION STARTS HERE' read the sign. Under a row of glass cases, museum-style, Uncle Harry's life was chronicled. The infant, the school-boy, the barmitzvah boy, serving in the family's fruit-shop, the political activist at open-air rallies . . . It was all there. The reality of Harry's life, as we all knew it. But there were other photographs displayed.

Harry posing proudly with Churchill, Roosevelt and Stalin at the Yalta Conference.

Harry having tea with Sigmund Freud.

Harry sharing a joke with Albert Einstein.

Harry shaking hands with Lenin.

Harry dancing with Ginger Rogers.

Harry singing with Bing Crosby.

Harry dining with Marilyn Monroe.

It was obvious that Harry had crudely superimposed his own photograph in every case. He had talked many times of his obsession with celebrities and fame and even, on occasion, of the possibility that he himself might become a living legend. But it was not to be.

By a small table, a card showing a fist smashing a swastika indicated the section 'THE FIGHT AGAINST FASCISM'. On the table there were two exhibits.

(A) Brick thrown by Harry Brown at Oswald Mosley in Cable Street, London, 3.00 p.m. May 9th, 1936

(B) Brick thrown by Oswald Mosley at Harry Brown in Cable Street, London, 3.05 p.m. May 9th, 1936

Harry had often told me about his trip to London in 1936, that fateful year. 'Fascists. Don't talk to me about those bastards. I did my bit, Arnold, don't say I didn't. May 5th, 1936. The Spanish Civil War broke out. I rushed to Sweden. No sense of direction. Then I rushed to London. May 10th, 1936, the Harrods sale. I personally fought

with the fascist leader, Oswald Mosley, over the last
cashmere pullover.'

I've always thought that if the European Allies had been aware of what my uncle was trying to do that day in Harrods, then perhaps the Second World War could have been averted. And that's not only my opinion. It was Uncle Harry's opinion too.

I had come to the end of the exhibition, but on the wall near the bed, I noticed there was a gold-framed inscription in Hebrew. The title was short but impressive.

MY URGENT MESSAGE TO THE WORLD

I took the parchment out of its frame and carefully tucked it into my inside pocket. Maybe the rabbi conducting the funeral service could translate Harry's last momentous testament for me. I suddenly felt sad for Harry and his unrealised dreams. As I was leaving the flat, I glanced back at the rocking-horse. I decided to have a wee shot on it. Cheer myself up. I wanted to feel what it was like to be a ninety-nine-year-old child.

It felt great.

7   The night class

The night class at number 15 Abbotsford Place was jam-packed with immigrants. Only the very ambitious ones in the Gorbals were brave enough to attend. They had taken the precaution of studying the new language on the boat coming over. The majority were content to get by with the odd phrase or two, clinging desperately to the Yiddish of the Old Country. That was hardly surprising, considering the impenetrably thick Glasgow accent they encountered everywhere on the streets. Most would wait until their sons and daughters went to school. Parents *can* learn from children . . .

As he was so quick on the uptake, Herschel became the obvious choice to be the family representative at the 'Welcome to Glasgow' series of evening lectures. When you're trying to make it in a new country, you've got to be told the facts, Jimmy.

The lecturer, Mr Andrew McTavish, chalked on the blackboard

WELCOME TO GLASGOW

Tell us everything, Mr McTavish.

He then wrote

GLESGA

'G-L-E-S-G-A. That's another way of spelling the name of this great city, the Second City of the British Empire. Let me first of all say that you are now living in one of the world's leading industrial centres. One in four of the world's ships and steam locomotives is built here on the Clyde. In the past, we have welcomed other newcomers, like the Highlanders after what was called the "Clearances". Luckily we got the Highlanders instead of the sheep. And, of course, we also welcomed into our midst the Irish, who came here after their potato crops failed. And now we are delighted to welcome your people, the Jews, into our community.'

The audience clapped appreciatively.

'But I must be frank. It's not going to be easy for you. There are some customs and traditions which strangers like yourselves will find difficult to understand. I will try to outline the situation as simply as possible.'

He chalked on the board. FOOTBALL (FITBA). 'I will elaborate. There are two great clubs in this city. There's RANGERS. Their ground is Ibrox, team colour light blue, and religion Protestant. And then there's CELTIC. Their ground is Parkhead, their team colour emerald green, and religion Catholic. Oh yes, I nearly forgot. Always remember in Scotland, Protestants are known as "Proddies" and Catholics as "Papes". I'll write that down for you – '

PRODDIES
PAPES

'It is also vital to remember at all times that the Proddies support Rangers and the Papes support Celtic. I'll have to be blunt, lads and lasses. There's a minority of people here in our city, who are what is known as "headcases". But, I repeat, they are a minority.' Mr McTavish chalked up the word 'HEADCASES' on the board. 'In other words, trouble-makers. It obviously follows that it is essential to be able to identify who are Proddies and who are Papes. To confuse the two groups could place you in a life-threatening situation. Therefore, I suggest for your own safety that if you are asked to comment on the result of any match between Rangers and Celtic, it is absolutely

crucial to know firstly which team the person you are talking to supports. And secondly, who won the match, or if
it was just a draw. It is very important to know: a mistake
could have serious consequences. A slight, intended or
otherwise, could leave you in some cases with serious
injuries to head, face, chest or legs . . .

'And now, another important point in this connection.
If you are passing through the Gorbals and you see at a
street corner a group of either Rangers or Celtic supporters
assembling, it is etiquette *not* to stare at them.

'The next point I want to bring up here is the "bevvy".
I'll write it down for you.'

He chalked it up on the board. B-E-V-V-Y. 'As used
in the phrase "Ah'm goin' oot to have a wee bevvy".
In other words, a wee dram. A drink. Now I know that
your people only imbibe on religious occasions. You are,
in effect, teetotallers. But here in Scotland, the working
man is traditionally thirsty at the end of a hard day's work,
or even if he isn't working, as sometimes does happen.
And the Scots, of course, were the ones who invented
the most famous drink of them all, whisky. I think I have
made it clear how important drink is to the Scottish
character. Is it any wonder that many Glaswegians hold
teetotallers in such great contempt? So here I must give
you another warning about one of our oldest traditions.
In Glasgow, we've always enjoyed the ancient ceremony
of throwing teetotallers *into* pubs on Saturday nights. I
would advise you not to resist the wishes of the Scottish
working people. If you allow yourselves to be projected
into, say, "The Saracen's Head", and partake of a wee sip
of whatever is offered to you, you will allay suspicions
that you are spurning hospitality.

'And now Nationalism.'

He chalked the word big and bold on the blackboard.

'The Scots have had many battles with many other nations in the past, but the number one enemy is "The Auld Enemy", England. In Scotland, the English are loathed. No denying it. We hate the buggers . . . Always have and always will. Because of this fact, the worst thing you can do to a Scots person is to attribute the many achievements of his fellow countrymen and women to these English bastards. So as to help you make no embarrassing mistakes, here is a list of Scottish discoveries, past, present and future . . . (I know a very remarkable fortune-teller in the Trongate).'

Mr McTavish walked over to a second larger blackboard and started to list the roll of honour, tears running down his face.

> THE MOTOR TYRE – John Boyd Dunlop
> THE BICYCLE – Kirkpatrick Macmillan
> THE TELEPHONE – Alexander Graham Bell
> TELEVISION – John Logie Baird
> PENICILLIN – Alexander Fleming
> CHLOROFORM – James Young Simpson

Mr McTavish took out a handkerchief from his pocket and dabbed his eyes. 'I'm sorry. Ladies and gentlemen. The mention of so many Scottish geniuses makes me very emotional. Bear with me, please. I'm obliged to tell you of one more custom which you should know about.

'Every 12th July in Glasgow, there's a march by the Protestants through the streets of the city. Pipers. Flute players, drummer boys. Everyone in their regalia, carrying banners. It's to commemorate the victory of the Proddies over the Papes in 1690. William of Orange was the Proddie leader and that's why it's called "The Orange Walk". Now here's

the point. The march cannot be interrupted or impeded.
So, if you are on the pavement when the march goes by, *stay there and remember, do not attempt to cross the street.* This is Glasgow's Highway Code.

'And now some *good* news for you. After the Orange Walk, sometimes fights break out. Jackets are torn, trousers are ripped, buttons are lost. I know that many of you are tailors, so you might find yourselves inundated with lots of repair jobs. Yes, the Orange Walk could be good for business, so it's not all doom and gloom I'm giving you.

'At the end of each lecture, I'll be introducing you to a well-known Glasgow phrase. That way, you'll be able to participate in the way of life of this great city. I will now write on the blackboard: AWAY AND BILE YOUR HEID. This indicates that you are so angry with someone and have so little respect for them, you are requesting them to go off and boil their head.'

Mr McTavish was coming to the end of his lecture. 'We've covered a lot of ground tonight. I have tried to tell you about the dangers you may encounter. But please do not get the impression that we are a city of violence. The vast majority of our citizens are decent and law-abiding. They want you to share with them all the delights that Glasgow can offer. The fine parks, the magnificent galleries and museums, the elegant tea-rooms, the music-halls, the theatres. Welcome to Glasgow!'

Herschel's hand shot up. 'And also you should say, "Welcome to Glesga!" '

'You catch on quick, Herschel.'

The class enjoyed the exchange and clapped their hands in appreciation. After all, they understood for the first time that they were now citizens of both Glasgow and Glesga.

8   Glenduffhill

We hide the dead away in corners. Out of sight, out of mind, Jimmy. Cemeteries are usually relegated to the outskirts of cities and the Glenduffhill Jewish Cemetery is in Shettleson at the far east end of Glasgow. If it's a conspiracy theory you're after, you could call it a Jewish plot, Jimmy. The burial grounds are overlooked by tombstones in the sky. Architects refer to them as tower blocks.

On the nineteenth floor two women looked curiously down on the proceedings.

'Anythin' decent oan telly?'

'Naw. That Joan Crawford we've seen twice before.'

'Gi's a fag.'

'Here.'

'Ta.'

'Where d'ye think we go tae when we're deid?'

'Search me. Havnae got a clue. No wan knows. It's a' pure guess-work.'

'Yon Catholics. They say ye go to Hell if ye've done bad.'

'No wonder they're doon in the chapel a' the time. They're dead feart.'

'Aye. And a' that confessin' their sins.'

'Daft buggers. Surely the whole bloody point of a sin is tae keep it tae yersel. Stands tae reason.'

'Aye. No doot aboot it.'

'Ah'd hate to be deid.'

'You said it.'

'Let's have a keek at the binocs.'

'Any sign o' mourners?'

'Aye. Just comin' oot of that wee hall. Mind you, it's no a great turn-oot.'

'Ah hope when ah die, there'll be lots of punters.'

'Well. Ah'll be there. Fur sure.'

'Aye, so ye will. Mind you – '

'Uhuh?'

'That's assumin' ah die first . . .'

'Ye're right. It's a' a lottery, death.'

'Aye. But ye dinnae havtae buy a ticket.'

'They jist arrived at the graveyard. Christ! Whit in God's name is that?'

'Whit is it?'

'That wee guy in the beard. Must be the rabbi. Ah dinnae believe it. It's like Chipperfield's circus doon ther. The rabbi's oan *stilts*.'

'Whit?'

'Ah tell ya. He's oan *stilts*.'

'Stilts? Aw c'mon. Ye're havin' me oan.'

'Naw. Have a wee keek yersel'.'

'Ma Goad. Ye're right. And two a' the mourners are helpin' him keep his balance.'

'Whit's happin' noo?'

'He's fallen intae the grave! Naw . . . they've jist caught him in time.'

'Yon Jews. Talk aboot strange customs. Daft buggers.'

'Aye. They're a bit soft in the heid, if ye ask me.'

'Ma God. He's readin' from a book. He's doin' the *service* oan stilts!'

'Let's ca' it a day.'

'Ye're right. Let's ca' it a day. Daft wee Jews.'

'Aye. Daft wee Jews.'

'Here.'

'Whit?'

'Yon heaven. Whit d'ye think it's like?'

'Och, ah dinnae ken. Mind ye. Must be a fair wack o' sun there.'

'Aye. Probably like Majorca.'

Every time I go back to Glenduffhill, I remember Uncle Harry's crusade against smoking. Glasgow has the highest incidence of deaths from lung cancer and coronary thrombosis in the western world. 'WHA'S LIKE US?' It's

not surprising the Scots have always flocked to the uni-
versity to study medicine. There's always been a lot of disease to peer at under the microscope in these parts, Jimmy.

In 1951, Harry wrote to the Ministry of Health urging them that the public had to be alerted to the dangers of cigarettes. He proposed that all smokers should be buried in packs of tens or twenties. The authorities never took up Harry's idea, but, of course, to be ignored is often the fate of visionaries.

Our tiny group of mourners had assembled in the cemetery. There were a number of cousins of the family and their sons, Harry's oldest friend, Callum Clark, and inevitably Auntie Sophie, who had chosen to wear her football strip. And then there was Kirsty, the young actress who had read bedtime stories to Uncle Harry in the last few years of his life.

A *minyan* is a quorum of ten *male* adults, the minimum requirement for congregational prayers. Children under thirteen years of age do not count. And neither do women. Thanks for nothing, Moses . . . To make up the numbers, two professional mourners had been roped in.

When you haven't got a *minyan*, do not fear.
Why not ring up Rent-A-Tear?

As the nearest male relative, I had to say Kaddish, the mourner's prayer. I stumbled over the Hebrew words, which I hadn't read in years. Talking to God is like everything else, Jimmy. You need practice.

9   Remembering Harry

Rabbi Maurice Freedman began his address. As he did so, I noticed a tall woman slip quietly in at the back. Her face was completely hidden by a dark veil.

'My dear friends. We are assembled today to mark the end of a good man's life. Harry Brown was a *mensh*. You see, life is like waiting at a bus-stop. You can wait in the cold for years for a Messiah to turn up, then suddenly three Messiahs turn up at the same time. Yes. Life is a journey and in Harry's case, I'm sure the destination is Heaven. Sometimes we get on the wrong bus. Sometimes we get on the right bus. Sometimes we get off too early. And sometimes we get off too late. If we are lucky, we get a seat all the way. But sometimes we have to stand. Yes, my dear friends, we are all passengers travelling along the road of life. Occasionally, the bus is full and we have to think of others less fortunate than ourselves. That old infirm person standing over there, that young mother getting on with an infant in her arms. So we have to ask ourselves. Should I give up *my* seat so that *their* journey will be that little easier? Yes, life is about giving up seats. Which brings me quite neatly, even though I say it myself, to Harry Brown. Harry devoted his entire life to thinking of others. He *always* gave up his seat. No matter what the occasion. Caring, selfless, sensitive. That was Harry Brown.' He paused. 'I'm afraid I now have to temporarily stop the service at this point. The wishes of the dead have to be respected, but unfortunately, these stilts are proving to be very uncomfortable.'

The rabbi jumped down to the security of the ground and walked a little distance to stretch his arms and legs for a minute. Looking a little sheepish, he then clambered back onto the stilts, which were held up by myself and Callum Clark. Rabbi Freedman's weight was incredibly light. Was it possible David, Harry's angel, was helping us out?

'Excuse me for that interruption,' he said. 'Now let me tell you more about Harry Brown. His campaigns against war, fascism, poverty and, of course, smoking, will always be remembered.

48 As will his tireless efforts to introduce into the National Health Service the radical concept of Laughter Clinics, where clowns and comedians could be employed to lift the spirits of the sick and the depressed. But again, the powers that be didn't want to know. In the same way they also ignored his pleas for "Worry-Kiosks" to be installed on the street corners of every city, town and village in the country: havens where the troubled could casually walk in and unburden themselves to trained counsellors. And finally, who amongst us here today will ever forget his campaign to bring in EEC legislation to persuade the large supermarket chains to stock *single* toilet-rolls? He was a man always ahead of his time. But luckily, the powers that be *did* eventually embrace one of his revolutionary ideas: the Alleyway of a Thousand Questions.'

After the coffin was lowered into the grave, the framed photographs of Freud, Marx and Einstein were also buried, together with a winning bingo card on which thirty-two was encircled; a number that has symbolic significance according to the Kabbalah. Uncle Harry's last wishes had been strictly adhered to. It was the least the world could do for a man who had done so much for the world.

As we all walked slowly and sadly away from the grave, I decided to ask Rabbi Freedman to translate the Hebrew message Harry had left in his flat. He glanced at the writing quickly.

'This is all gibberish. The ravings of a very old man. Complete and utter nonsense. What a tragedy when a fine mind like Harry's disintegrates into madness. But if you don't mind, I'll keep it anyway.'

I was confused. If the message was as incoherent as Rabbi Freedman indicated, why would he want to keep it? I was just about to query this with him when there

was a muffled ringing from his overcoat pocket. To my
amazement, he whipped out a portable phone.

'Rabbi Freedman here. Yes. Just finishing at Glenduffhill. Catch the six p.m. train to Edinburgh? Hmm. Yes. I see. Rabbi Lionel Blue has dropped out? Mmm. To record a *Thought for the Day*? Yes. I think I can make it.'

He returned the portable phone to his overcoat pocket and sprinted off to his car, shouting over his shoulder, 'Long Life! It's my agent. Must dash!'

As we were leaving the burial grounds, I glanced over to a group of tombstones on the other side of the gates. There in the dusk, a heroin addict was openly shooting up. On the outside wall, someone had daubed 'Jewish Scum' and a swastika sign. As Harry often said, 'Happiness – the search continues.' I then realised the veiled woman had vanished.

Clutching an imaginary microphone, Auntie Sophie began to speak to no one in particular. 'And so we mourn the end of the life of Harry Brown. It is now five thirty p.m., the congregation have dispersed, but his memory will always linger on. Sophie Brown. *News at Ten*. Glenduffhill Cemetery, Glasgow.'

10 Call Sam Levine

I stayed overnight in Harry's flat. I suppose it wasn't that surprising, but I dreamed about Rabbi Freedman, urgent-message snatcher. There he was, perched on top of the tower block overlooking Glenduffhill Cemetery, clutching a twenty-foot-long portable phone. Suddenly he clicked his fingers and a golden eagle sailed down from nowhere, like a taxi being hailed. The rabbi clambered onto the eagle's back, portable phone and all, and the huge bird soared quickly out of sight.

I wondered who the veiled mourner was. There had been rumours over the years of Harry's involvement with a Roman Catholic woman who worked as a 'parkie' in Queen's Park.

After breakfast, I dried the dishes with Uncle Harry's favourite tea-towel, the one with Albert Einstein's face on it. We all know the famous equation: $E = MC^2$ = Washing-up liquid. I wondered how Rabbi Freedman's *Thought For The Day* had gone. Did it contain the usual adages? Media rabbis enjoy relating the traditional talmudic jokes. They're fortunate people. They can use material that's over five thousand years old. As a comedian, I should be so lucky.

The phone rang. Who else could it be but Auntie Sophie? 'Strathclyde Police are today investigating the disappearance of Rabbi Maurice Freedman after he failed to return to his home in Glasgow, following a BBC Radio broadcast in Edinburgh. Sophie Brown. *News at Ten*. Glasgow.' The phone clicked. She was gone.

52 Obviously I now had to stay on in the city until Freedman's shenanigans had been explained. I needed help, professional help, and I immediately thought of Sam Levine, an old school pal. He was always a bit of a loner, never part of the gang in the playground. An outsider. Perhaps it was not surprising he became a private eye. There are some job ambitions you can't discuss with a careers officer, Jimmy.

Sam had already heard the news about Rabbi Freedman on the grapevine and we arranged to meet at his downtown office in St Vincent Street. I had an hour to kill, so I strolled down the long Victoria Road past Eglinton Toll towards the Gorbals. On a wall there was a crudely daubed message, 'PAKIS OUT'. New immigrants. New scapegoats.

The Gorbals, where the Jews came to live, work, and of course, eat in their own special kosher way. Pork? No way. Rather sensible when you realise it's the most common carrier of the parasites of the deadly disease, trichinosis. So it's not all mumbo-jumbo, Jimmy. And wasn't it lucky that the Almighty guided the Jews to Scotland? Scotland, the country whose longest river, the Tay, was home to the spawning salmon, which eventually turned into smoked salmon – for some Jews, the delicacy above all delicacies. Talk about serious serendipity, Jimmy.

Harry once told me his own deeply-held beliefs on the subject of food. 'Arnold, always remember the Jewish dietary laws as set out in the Kabbalah: Never eat in a restaurant where the waiters have cloven feet.' I've never forgotten that, but I must say it does get me into so many incidents in restaurants, trying to get the shoe off to check it.

As I crossed over Jamaica Bridge into town, I recalled that a young boy in the Gorbals called Herschel Lizerbram was miraculously transformed one day into someone by the name of Harry Brown.

'Och, ye canna ca' the young lad Herschel if he's sittin' at a desk in school next to Angus, Tam and Andy. It's jist no fair on him.'

But Abraham and Sarah were not happy . . . 'Did Moses change his name?' Point taken, but then again, Moses never wanted to grow up to captain Scotland and thrash England 5–1 at Wembley in 1928.

'And Abraham's got the ball, he passes it on to Moses. Moses, a quick flick to Ezekiel running up on the right touchline. Ezekiel dribbles round one, two, three English defenders. Oh yes, the English are in deep trouble here at Wembley! And now Ezekiel lobs the ball into the English penalty area and, my goodness, there's Moses thrusting himself up, up, up, with a *magnificent* header into the goalmouth. And it's a G-O-A-L! Just listen to the Scots crowd roaring out their hero's name: MOS-*ES*! MOS-*ES*! MOS-*ES*! EA-*SY*! EA-*SY*! EA-*SY*! WE ARE THE PEOPLE!'

No way, Jimmy.

11 Questions

I walked up Bath Street towards Sauchiehall Street, the long thoroughfare that cuts through the centre of Glasgow. A lot of punters say that Princes Street in Edinburgh is much more elegant. If you twisted my arm in the wrong direction, I might have to agree. But so what, Jimmy. It was Glasgow and not Edinburgh that was chosen as the 1990 European City of Culture. I'm sorry, Edinburgh, a castle above a shopping complex was simply not enough. And quite right too, Jimmy. That military Tattoo is just a blatant excuse to celebrate war to the sound of fireworks and bagpipes . . .

Whenever I return to Glasgow, I always enjoy walking the streets. Mind you, I must say I also find great pleasure in strolling down the occasional crescent. On this occasion I had a slight accident. I walked into a lamp-post. It was so dark inside that lamp-post, I decided to walk out again. Sometimes the council just don't do their job properly. I then looked over my favourite shoulder. I had this vague feeling I was being followed. Maybe it was the authorities. They keep tabs on all us dissidents. Something to do with our protests against the iniquitous Poll Tax. They dumped

it on the Scots one year earlier than the rest of the coun-
try. I was so livid about this injustice, I decided to make a stand, just as Uncle Harry had taught me to do all his life. On the section of the Poll Tax form where you had to define your relationship with the other persons in the household, I put: 'Going through a bad patch.'

And I elaborated. 'PS. We hope to resolve the situation shortly.'

I think it's always important to give the government hope.

A face loomed up in front of me. 'Can you spare a deposit on a wee flat near the Uni, Jimmy?' (In a recent survey in *The Scotsman*, it was revealed that the most popular name chosen to address strangers in Glasgow is Jimmy. In these parts, a name like Tristan, Peregrine or Justin is definitely not on. In the same survey, the second most popular term of approach turned out to be 'Hey you, son – ')

To save him getting involved in protracted negotiations with estate agents, building societies and solicitors, I took the easy way out and side-stepped my property-aspiring friend.

A man in a tartan cap sidled up to me and asked: 'Have you got a meat pie on you, Jimmy?'

I made a quick body-search. You never know. I've carried a meat pie for months without knowing it. Sadly, he was out of luck. As it happens I never carry a meat pie on a Tuesday. But to be fair, how was he to know that?

Then another man rushed up to me and said: 'Have you got an encyclopaedia on you, Jimmy?'

'What are you on about, man?' I enquired. I know how to speak to them.

'I want to settle an argument.'

'An argument? What argument?' I asked, incredulously.

'Well, my mate Sandy says you've got an encyclopaedia on you.'

We're a very educated race, we Scots. But there is the question of stereotypes. Rab C. Nesbitt and all that TV exposure. Do you think that all Scotsmen go trawling round the streets in a vest? Drunken louts? No way. Let me just say one thing. Wasn't it a lucky break for civilisation that someone like Alexander Graham Bell managed to sober up just long enough to invent the telephone?

A man in a kilt came ambling towards me. (Was he a professional Scotsman employed by the Tourist Board, I asked myself?) He was carrying a heavy-looking volume which, as he got nearer, I realised was an encyclopaedia. I looked around for the man who had been trying earlier to settle an argument, but he had vanished. Encyclopaedia-carrier came up to me and put his face right up to mine, almost touching. I'm talking *tension*.

And he said: 'Are you looking at me, Jimmy?'

I couldn't make up my mind, so I ran away.

A few minutes later, I found myself in a narrow lane. To my astonishment, the same thing seemed to be happening again.

A man dashed up to me in a clear state of agitation and asked: 'Why is it that every day there's the exact number of stories to fill the newspapers?'

The sheer intellectual and philosophical breadth of this question intrigued me. Who was this man? And why had he chosen to come to this particular lane at this particular time to ask this particular question? Then I suddenly realised I had stumbled by chance into the public debating-forum Uncle Harry had fought so hard to establish in the last few years of his life. The man had come here because he knew this was the very place where *this* mystery might be solved. I was standing in THE ALLEYWAY OF A THOUSAND QUESTIONS . . .

12 An encounter at the January sales

Later, as I was nearing Sam Levine's office in St Vincent Street, I decided to check into the answering machine I had installed in Uncle Harry's flat. Because of the Rabbi Freedman episode, I thought it might come in useful and I was dead right. There was an important message. An elderly female Dublin voice, soft and lilting.

'Arnold Brown? You don't know me, Arnold, but I was at the funeral. Harry and I go back a long way. In fact we were friends for almost fifty years. Look, I don't quite know how to put this, but I think there's something you should know. Just before he died, Harry told me something very strange. He said he was leaving behind something quite invaluable. A precious autograph. Apparently it's all explained in some message he left behind in Calder Street. Oh yes, and there was something else. Now let's see, I wrote it down for you. Oh, here it is. "Clickety-click, Freedman's sick." That's everything. Maybe we'll meet sometime. Bye, Arnold.'

So perhaps the woman in the veil was Harry's old love, the one we had all heard about, whom he'd met at the Plaza Ballroom in 1946. But she wasn't to know I had already heard the autograph story. Harry had told me all about it one wet September afternoon.

'It's been a long life, Arnold. As you're well aware, I began with Socialism, drifted into Buddhism, and ended up with rheumatism. The world today is in complete chaos. Take global warming. I did my bit. I bought a catalytic converter and every week I used to buy unleaded petrol. Mind you, I haven't got a car . . . But I still believe it's important to show an example to the younger generation. And, of course, there's also war, poverty, disease. But religion doesn't seem to have helped any of these problems. On the contrary, it's made things even worse. Take the Pope and all that *mishegoss* he spouts about birth-control. Doesn't he know that the population grows every month by more than *seven million*? Frankly, I'd listen to him if he pontificated on a subject he *really* knows about. Like the taste of airport tarmac. No Arnold, I've never had time for any religion, until recently that is, when something quite extraordinary happened.

'I was walking around the Princes Square shopping mall at the top of Buchanan Street about two and a half years ago. I always go to the January sales, look around, share in the excitement. I was having a tea in a quiet part of a little café. My table was slightly out of the way from the rest. A large palm tree practically hid me from all the other customers. As usual, I was deep in thought. I remember I was thinking about dolphins and whether I should adopt one. Anyway, I looked up and got the shock of my life. I couldn't believe my eyes. There, standing in front of me, was God! Of course, I recognised him straight away by the long white beard and the "I ran the world" T-shirt he was wearing. I was flabbergasted. Dumbfounded. Then I blurted out the question any mortal would have asked in such a situation. "God – what are you doing here?"

'I'll always remember his reply. "Harry, have you seen the bargains?"

'He told me he would have liked to stay and chat, but apparently there was some crisis he had to deal with. A famine, or some emergency like that, I think. He was about to leave and that was when I remembered my autograph book. I always carry it around. You never know when you might bump into someone really famous. So I asked him to sign it. And he also took time to write a personal dedication to me. Very courteous, I thought. As soon as he finished, he said: "Sorry it's been so short, Harry. Got to fly." And he did, right out an open window.'

13   126 St Vincent Street

126 St Vincent Street is a solid stone Victorian office building. As Sam's office was on the sixth floor, I waited for the lift. Three Suits got in with me. They were babbling on about accountancy matters. All that money-mania doesn't do your sex life any favours, Jimmy. As an ex-accountant myself, I know that some of the Balance-sheet Boys even talk about the strength of the pound during foreplay. And of course, there are some who think that talking about the strength of the pound *is* foreplay . . . To be honest, in these matters I still advocate the monetarist position. That's the one with the bank manager on top. I'm talking Big Bang, Jimmy.

The Otis lift creaked ominously as its old ropes slid round the pulleys. It suddenly stopped just before the sixth floor and refused to budge. None of the other passengers knew what to do in the circumstances. Then I remembered what Uncle Harry told me he had done many years ago in a similar crisis. I took complete command of the situation. I led the screaming. That's what this country needs. Leaders.

Fortunately, Sam Levine heard my shouts and came running out of his office to investigate. Puffing furiously at

a cigarette as if his death depended on it, he jiggled the
bars of the lift for a few minutes and reluctantly it agreed
to move slowly to the safety of the sixth floor.

Sam was short, dumpy, balding and bespectacled. Life's
not perfect, Jimmy . . . The lettering on his office door was
a cruel comment on our uncaring society.

SAM LEVINE
Private Detective Agency
No DSS cases accepted

As I told him all the latest developments, Sam scribbled
notes on a pad in silence. When I finished, he smiled at
me, relaxed back in his chair and said: 'Everyone respected
Harry Brown. He was a dreamer, some even said he was
crazy. But remember, they laughed at Newton, Darwin
and once, just once, at Max Bygraves here in Glasgow.
Mind you, that was at the Empire, which was always a
graveyard for English comedians. But that's another
story . . . Yes, Harry was a *mensh*. I'm honoured you
have chosen me to solve this Rabbi Freedman conundrum.
I've already made a few preliminary enquiries about him,
but I haven't come up with much so far, apart from the
sermon allegations.'

I was confused. 'Sermon allegations?'

'Yes. It's a small community here in Glasgow. Rumours
fly around fast. A lot of Freedman's congregation have
been complaining of blatant plagiarism. They'd listen one
morning to Rabbi Lionel Blue on BBC Radio Four's *Thought
for the Day*, and the following Shabbos, Rabbi Freedman's
sermon would cover exactly the same topic. Sometimes
he'd even have the chutzpah to use an identical meta-
phor here, the same talmudic reference there. Nothing
earth-shattering, you understand. But there were rumbles.

64 People were beginning to talk. Sometimes even during his sermons. Of course, Freedman vehemently denied all the allegations. Swore it was just a case of coincidence each time. But anyway, the way I read things at the moment is that there's possibly something much more serious going on than just simply stealing sermon ideas.'

Sam promised to let me know as soon as he discovered anything. As I left, he told me he'd work day and night on the case and added: 'The strange fact is that my father wanted me to become a rabbi. But I told him at the time I didn't fancy the short hours.'

14   The pub

Some time ago, I wandered into a pub in South London. I think it was called 'The Tattooed Wally'. I was carrying my Harrods carrier-bag. I was flaunting it, so that everyone in the pub would notice. I think it's important for the working class to know what they're missing. Suddenly from behind the counter, the barman started shouting at me: 'Awlright, my son? Awlright? Awlright?'

I thought to myself. That's not my father.

Then he asked me: 'What's in the bag?'

Well, to provoke him, I replied: 'Jim Davidson.'

　　　He got angry. I got angry. That's what happens in pubs. The drink makes the customers that bit more aggressive. Sometimes fighting breaks out, or even worse. Which leads to headlines in local papers. 'Affray outside Croydon pub. Fourteen injured.' That's why I prefer quieter places. Like cafés, coffee-shops, tea-rooms. I'm a *patisserie* kind of guy. You never hear of an affray outside a tea-room.

　　'You've just spilled my Earl Grey.'

　　'Darjeeling is *much* more aromatic than Assam.'

　　'I'll see you and your croissant outside, matey . . .'

15 Tea-rooms

I like sitting in tea-rooms. The ritual of the tea and the cakes and the croissants is so relaxing. But what I enjoy most of all is overhearing other people's conversations. I suppose you might say I'm a bit of a sociologist on the side. On the other hand, you may prefer to call me a nosey bastard.

I was now in downtown Sauchiehall Street, having a swanky Earl Grey tea and a croissant. The setting: the Willow Tea-Room, the creation of the great Scottish architect, Charles Rennie Mackintosh. Inside, his influence is everywhere. Even nowadays, the wait-resses are specially selected for their unusually high backs. Of course, it was soon after Mackintosh design-ed his revolutionary waitress-shape that he came up in 1903 with

the even better idea of the elegant high-back chair we all know and love.

It was great to be in the Willow, but I must admit there are other tea-rooms in Glasgow where decorum is a word they seldom use. Sometime ago, I was in a tea-room where the service was so bad I had to send the waitress back. At the table next to mine there was a small bald man. It was high summer, but he was wearing a plastic mac. The wee guy called the waitress over. Half an hour later, she came to his table. I pricked up my ears.

'Can I help you?'

'See that notice, hen?'

'There's quite a few notices. Which one are you talking about?'

'That wan over there: "The Management refuses to accept responsibility for coats, hats, umbrellas, etcetera".'

'I'm busy,' she snapped. 'What's your problem?'

'Whit ah want to know is this . . . Dis that etcetera include us punters?'

There's a thirst for knowledge in Glasgow you can never quench.

Back in the Willow Tea-Room, I looked down at my
plate. All that remained of my croissant was a few sad
flakes.

At the next table to mine, a small bald man in a plastic
mac sat down. He ordered tea, scones and marmalade.
There was something weird in the way he emphasised the
word 'marmalade'. I pricked up my ears, as I have every
right to do.

'See that notice over there, hen,' he said to the waitress.
' "You don't have to be mad to work here but it helps"?
That's no true. See ma brother. He applied for a job here
wance. He's as daft as a brush. He didnae get the job, so
it disnae help to be roon the bend . . .'

In the corner, an old man in a cloth cap nodded in
agreement, then suddenly stood up and loudly announced
that he was taking his chocolate éclair for a walk in the
Botanic Gardens.

Things were hotting up. Anything could happen now.
An old woman hid her hat under the table. It was made
of pheasant feathers jutting out of a cluster of imitation fruit.

She looked like a veteran of many tea-room skirmishes and knew the score. She ordered her sixth potato scone of the afternoon, perhaps realising this was the best thing to do under the circumstances.

It was all great value for money, but I still felt peckish. I noticed in the window a particularly large cream cake. I said to myself: 'I want to dominate that cream cake.' Casually I asked the waitress to bring the cream cake over to me, managing to suppress any trace of excitement in my voice.

As she placed the cake in front of me, her onyx crucifix swung around and caught me on the end of my nose. She leaned over and whispered: 'I hope you don't mind me asking, sir, but what exactly are you going to do with that cream cake?'

I managed to maintain my composure.

'I'm just going to eat it, of course,' I explained airily. 'What are you getting at?' As she was about to answer, I suddenly realised that the little figure on her crucifix was Elvis Presley.

'Well, sir,' she said, 'we had a gentleman in here many years ago. Like you, he ordered a cream cake. I served him myself. As I put it before him, he began to

scream hysterically. Although it was quite a while ago,
I still remember his exact words. They came out almost animal-like, a frenzied scream. I've never heard that sound before from a human being. He kept repeating over and over again: "Cream cake, I am your master. You will do exactly as I say!" Of course, we called the police and after a struggle he was escorted away.'

'Hmm,' I said, 'what a fascinating story. But frankly, I can't see why you're telling *me* all this.'

'Well sir, the reason I'm bringing all this up is that you have an uncanny resemblance to that unfortunate gentleman.' Her face puckered up nervously and she asked: 'You're not by any chance related, are you?'

I suddenly remembered. Yes, it was here in the hallowed precincts of the Willow Tea-Room in 1976 that Uncle Harry had disgraced the entire Jewish Community by his outrageous breach of tea-room protocol. Urgent consultations had to be set up between Rabbi Greenbaum in Glasgow and the Anti-Menstruation Section of the Elders of Zion in London. An appeal fund was set up and enough money was quickly raised to send Uncle Harry away to Dunoon for three months to recuperate in the sea air.

Back in the Willow Tea-Room, I managed to convince the waitress that I certainly had no connection whatsoever with the gentleman who had created such a regrettable incident all those years ago. I leaned forward in my chair and began to eat my cream cake. But resisted any temptation to dominate it.

16   Heroes

I walked out of the Willow Tea-Room into Sauchiehall Street, leaving behind all the tormented souls in Diet-Hell.

A woman came towards me. I was struck by how thin she was. I noticed a small badge on her lapel 'Lose weight now. Ask me how.' I completely ignored her. My mind was on higher things.

Charles Rennie Mackintosh, for example, who was of course, much revered by Uncle Harry. Uncle Harry loved to read about great Scotsmen through the ages. He would walk down the street, proudly intoning their illustrious names: Robert Burns, Robert the Bruce, Bonnie Prince Charlie . . . One day, however, a passing feminist challenged him: 'What about great Scotswomen?'

Uncle Harry was so ashamed that he didn't open a history book for three months. Another man of Uncle Harry's generation might have ignored the remark. But in fact, Uncle Harry was an early feminist himself. Our family would often recount how, at a race-meeting in Ayr, he threw himself under a suffragette. Despite this brave stance, Harry was a lifelong bachelor and very shy with the opposite sex. It seemed likely that his involvement with the

woman in the veil had been his only serious relationship. A chance encounter in a ballroom one evening and your life is changed for ever, Jimmy.

Strangely enough, Harry's ballroom dancing career had started in a most unusual way. It was 1919. The huge demonstration walked down Argyle Street, heading for George Square and the City Chambers. Capitalism was on its knees, Jimmy. The socialist hero, John MacLean, carried the Red Flag. The excitement was unbelievable. For Harry it was too much. He rushed forward and snatched the flag from the leader's hands and marched with it at the front of the parade. Every eye was on Harry. He held the flag proudly aloft in the air and suddenly his march turned into a waltz, then a rumba and finally a tango. The crowd went wild. They knew they were seeing history being made. It was the first time that anyone had ever managed to bring the rhythm and elegance of the dance floor into political dissent.

And, of course, another great hero of Harry's was Alexander Fleming. He often enjoyed recounting how Flemmie was working late in the laboratory one evening, even then, a good Scot having a job and desperately trying to keep it. And not only that. Christmas was looming. The kids wanted expensive toys, so overtime pay was essential.

As the great man left to go home, he accidentally knocked over a beaker of liquid. In the morning he noticed on the bench a culture of mould. Under the microscope, Fleming was excited to see something strange: squiggly shapes he had never encountered before. Then it suddenly dawned on him. The molecular structure he was looking at under the microscope had exactly the same pattern as his underpants. Putting two and two together, Flemmie rolled up his sleeves and discovered penicillin. It's as easy as that, if you're a genius, Jimmy. Uncle Harry was fond of pointing out that if Flemmie had been an Englishman, he would have just cleaned up the mess.

17   The Rolls-Royce

Meanwhile in Sauchiehall Street, the exhaust fumes were making their favourite journey towards St Vincent Street and the Princess Margaret Hospital for Diseases of the Respiratory System. I was still on the pavement outside the Willow. Someone had attached the Scottish flag to a bollard on the traffic island. It was rippling defiantly in the carbon monoxide haze. Needless to say, devolution is a hot potato up here and the nationalists are demanding independence for all Scottish traffic islands by 1995.

I then noticed that a young woman and a baby had now come onto the island. She was smoking. I couldn't believe what happened next. The woman suddenly offered her cigarette to the baby, who took a puff and exhaled expertly. My mind was reeling. I was outraged. In no time this baby would have the heaviest cough in the crèche. I knew the dangers from first-hand experience. My own father was addicted to cigarettes. I always saw him behind a puff of smoke. Until the age of ten, I thought that he was a professional magician. Mind you, it was in those far-off days in the fifties when there was no proven medical link between smoking and advertising.

I jumped into action. 'Help! Social worker!' I yelled.

The cigarette still dangled from the baby's lower lip and the smoke rose and drifted away to join the exhaust fumes. I knew what I had to do. I darted forward in the direction of the island.

Suddenly something emerged gracefully from nowhere and crashed into me without even saying sorry. Just before I blacked out, I looked up and realised I'd been hit by a Rolls-Royce.

I'd been knocked out once before in my life. I was head-butted by a squirrel in Queen's Park. I think it was something to do with the fact that I was wearing my Third Lanark football scarf. Even today, sectarianism in the Glasgow animal kingdom is still a problem.

Coming to, I became aware of a Havana cigar hovering a few inches above me. 'Don't you dare give that cigar to the baby,' I screamed.

The face behind the cigar spoke. 'What baby? What's he on about?'

There was a crowd of bystanders peering down at me. I noticed the woman and the smoking baby had vanished.

18 Malkie

The cigar continued to hover over me. Its owner was becoming clearer through the smoke. A man in an executive overcoat with aggressive astrakahan lapels. He brought out his portable phone and dialled.

'MacDonald here. Sell my granny.'

The bystanders gave him a collective dirty look.

'I said, "Sell my granny"!' Here he paused and added: 'But not to the Japs.'

He turned to the crowd and said: 'Sentimental reasons.'

The bystanders nodded sympathetically.

Business over, MacDonald rounded on me: 'You just shot into the road like a daft snooker ball! You bampot – you dented the Rolls! Get your arse off that pavement and see the damage you've done.'

I knew I was dealing with some sort of psychopath. I decided to humour him. 'Look, I'm sorry.'

He shuddered. 'Sorry! I should bloody well hope you are. A man like me has to defraud one hell of a number of companies to acquire a car like this. They don't grow on trees, you know.'

I couldn't take my eyes off MacDonald's ears. They were

huge, maroon. I knew I'd seen them somewhere before. Then it dawned on me. This was Malkie MacDonald, once a fellow pupil at Queen's Park Senior Secondary. I now remembered the school had been very proud of Malkie's ears. The measurements were submitted to *The Guinness Book of Records*, but the application was turned down following the results of a drug test. Traces of steroids were found in the wax of the left ear.

A small bald man in a plastic mac stepped forward from the crowd. He took out a collapsible stool, unfolded it and sat down. Then he addressed the bystanders. 'Since the wife died, ah always carry a stool everywhere. Ye make so many new friends at accidents.'

Malkie ignored him. He was staring at me intently. 'Hold on. I thought I recognised you. You're Arnold Brown. We were in the same class at Queen's Park. Remember me – I'm Malkie. Red Malkie.'

Now it all clicked into place. Not only the school days, but afterwards. Malkie MacDonald, aka Red Malkie, used to sell the *Daily Worker* every Saturday morning outside the Central Station.

A woman in a green coat pushed her way to the front. 'You're that wee comic on the telly, are you no? Yer patter's like watter!'

Malkie turned on my disloyal fan. He had calmed down. 'I just don't understand some people,' he said fiercely, staring at her. 'The man's just been through an accident. Leave him alone. Let him rest for God's sake.'

At the front of the crowd, the man with the stool got up: 'Get oan with the bloody show! Whaur's the ambulance?'

The woman in green nodded. 'Yon's quite right – we havnae had the ambulance yet . . .'

A voice from the crowd shouted: 'Gi' us a joke, Arnold.'

I began my 'Growing Up In Glasgow' routine. 'My name's Arnold Brown. And why not?' I suddenly felt very dizzy and passed out.

19 The Glasgow Empire

By coincidence, my brief street gig had occurred only a few hundred yards away from the old site of the Glasgow Empire, the theatre where English comedians often came, but never conquered. Elephants seldom forget and it's the same with us comedians, Jimmy. The nightmare of a bad gig stays in the psyche for ever and sometimes even after that. Come to think of it, any elephant would have stood a better chance of winning over Saturday night audiences at the Empire than the doomed Sassenachs who tiptoed off to thunderous indifference. They kept returning to Glasgow, despite public demand. It's fair to say it was a case of a bond being established between performers and audiences. This could be accurately summed up in the one word. Resentment.

Uncle Harry always liked to talk about the world of show business. 'Entertainment? It's not like it was in my day, Arnold. Only yesterday, I read in the paper that scientists in the University of California are claiming to have invented an amazing micro-chip weighing less than half a gram. You just insert it into the ear and it stimulates the endorphins in exactly the same way that laughter does. Now they predict that one day comedians will be obsolete! And they call this progress! What next? Lasers up your nostrils for a great night out?

'I remember the old days when we all went to the music halls and the variety theatres. Live entertainment it was and the whole audience roared with delight at the jokes and the music and the speciality acts. You had this sense of being part of one community.

'Mind you, when the Jews first came to Glasgow, we were entering an alien culture we couldn't understand. So at first we were content just to go to the Yiddish Theatre at the Royal Princess's in Main Street. Songs and stories from the Old Country. Clinging to the past. You see, Arnold, you couldn't laugh at the jokes or understand the topics of the songs until you knew what tenement life was all about; the "stairheids", the "dunnies", the "middens". But as time went by, the Jews got used to the Glasgow ways and gradually they too began to go to the Empire, the Pavilion and the Metropole like everyone else did. These were the halls where working people enjoyed their evenings of glamour, an escape from the harsh routine of everyday lives.

'It was at the Glasgow Empire I started waiting outside the stage door with my autograph book, for it was the Empire that attracted the biggest stars. My particular favourite was Harry Lauder. I first saw him in the winter of 1922. I was at the front of the gallery in the sixpenny seats. I'll never forget that moment when he walked on and the orchestra struck up the opening notes of "I Love A Lassie". A roar of appreciation erupted from the crowd. He dominated the stage. Charisma from head to toe. Scotland's ambassador to the world.

'There's another story I must mention here, Arnold. It

was the summer of 1925. I read in the *Evening Times* that
Laurel and Hardy were coming to play at the Empire. The
day they arrived at Central Station, the whole place was
packed with fans waiting to welcome them. I happened to
know a ticket collector called Billy Moir and he let me stand
inside the barrier. The Royal Scot finally arrived at platform
five. Photographers' bulbs flashed everywhere. The crowd
surged forward and pandemonium broke out. Suddenly a
short man in a dark suit and a homburg emerged from
the mêlée. For some reason, he approached me and said
in broken English: "My name is Albert Einstein. Can you
direct me to the Central Hotel? I'm here to receive a hon-
orary doctorate from Glasgow University and I must say,
in all my years as a scientist, no other city in the world
has turned out in their thousands to pay homage to me.
I am deeply touched."

'Of course, I got Einstein to sign my autograph book,
but I didn't have the heart to tell him they'd all come to
see Laurel and Hardy.'

20 The trip to New York

That chance meeting in 1925 Uncle Harry had with Albert Einstein at Glasgow Central Station was remarkable enough. But nearly thirty years later, their paths were to cross once again in even more bizarre circumstances.

'One of my dreams, Arnold, was to see my face depicted on a postage stamp. Just like my heroes Freud, Marx and Einstein. To my way of thinking, that recognition is the highest accolade society can bestow on anyone. But alas it was not meant to be. All my life my ideas have never found acceptance, because they were always too ahead of their time. Except, of course, for the Alleyway of a Thousand Questions. And that was only because I happened to be very friendly with Jimmy Docherty in the Town Planning Department at Glasgow City Chambers. We were in the same Buddhist meditation group in Dixon Avenue.

'Perhaps my life would have turned out differently if our family had landed in America. America! That's always been the home of new ideas. I remember when the talkies came to Glasgow for the first time in 1929. It was Al Jolson in *The Singing Fool*. The queues stretched right round the block and it ran for months at the Green's Playhouse. That

was the biggest cinema in Europe at the time with seats for
nearly four and a half thousand people. It was the start of
my great love affair with all the stars on the silver screen.
I felt I knew America from the films and often told David,
my angel, how wonderful it would be to go there, but of
course, that was only a dream.

'Then one day in 1955, during the Fair Fortnight holiday,
he knocked on my door and said: "Harry. In two days' time
on Thursday, get up early at six a.m. As a treat, I'm taking
you to New York for the day."

' "Is that possible?" I said.

' "Harry, if you've got an angel at your service, anything's
possible," David replied.

'I told everyone that I was away to Dunoon for a
few days.

'We set off before dawn, and it was an incredible
journey. Luckily it was warm and dry and it only took
about six hours to cross the Atlantic. David always had
special powers to disguise himself as an ordinary human
being, so it was no problem walking around New York
with him. It was just like it was in the films, Arnold. The
skyscrapers were twice as tall as the tallest tower blocks
here in Glasgow. When you see the place for the first
time, it's quite unbelievable. The city hums with electric
energy. It's all around, in the buildings, the streets, the
people. We stopped in a deli on Twenty-Second Street
and ate the biggest smoked salmon sandwiches I'd ever
seen.

'As we walked out into the street again, David turned
round to me and said: "Harry, I've got a surprise for you.
We're going to the Waldorf Tower."

'I didn't know what he was talking about, but when
we got there I realised right away it must have been the

swankiest hotel in the city. "We're going to the twentieth floor, Room 2022," David whispered to me in the lift. I didn't ask questions. Well, you never did with David. You always keep *shtoom*. That's the deal with angels. We got to the twentieth floor, the top one. David pulled a key out of his pocket, turned the lock and we were inside this magnificent suite of rooms, velvet curtains, chandeliers, a four-poster. I'd never seen anything like it.

'David suddenly whispered to me: "Harry, they're coming. Quick, follow me into that cupboard."

'I was bewildered but I did as he said and squeezed in. We were surrounded by ballgowns and evening dresses. As I looked through the slats, the door opened and there in front of me in the room was the most intelligent man in the world, Albert Einstein, and with him was the most beautiful woman in the world, Marilyn Monroe. They were embracing. It was breathtaking. The two most famous people in the universe and I was in the same room as them! I can tell you, Arnold, it took all the will-power I could muster not to step out and ask for Marilyn's autograph. I think I've told you I'd already got Albert's at the Central Station way back in 1925. Marilyn was a vision of radiance to behold.

'Suddenly she drew apart from Albert and walked gracefully over to the record-player. And then the strangest thing happened. They started to dance closely together not to music, but to poetry. I think it was John Gielgud reading T. S. Eliot's "The Waste Land". It was very moving. Then Albert went over to the drinks cabinet and poured out two glasses of champagne. They sat down on the sofa and looked into each other's eyes. They were obviously so much in love.

'Marilyn spoke: "Albert, darling, please explain to me the Theory of Relativity."

'He said something and for the moment I just can't remember what it was. It might come back to me later . . .

'Then Marilyn said to Albert: "You're a man of the world, Albert. You've been around. Tell me about Glasgow."

'He thought about this for a second, then he began to talk about my home city. "It's a wonderful place. The striking architecture, the great ocean liners in the shipyards, the scientific and academic centres of learning. But best of all, the warm, friendly people. What a reception they gave me! I'll never forget it."

'Albert and Marilyn went into the next room and shortly afterwards we left the hotel and walked through the bright lights of Broadway. It had been the trip of a lifetime and we got back to Glasgow early next morning.'

There was still one thing that intrigued me. I asked Harry if he could remember Albert's reply when Marilyn asked him to explain the Theory of Relativity. Happily, Harry remembered.

'Ah yes, it all comes back to me now. Albert said to her: "I'm sorry, Marilyn. I never go that far on a first date." '

21 Ol' Blue Eyes

Before we go on, I want to get one thing straight, Jimmy. Uncle Harry is not the only one in the family who has dallied a few moments with the Truly Famous. I too have had such nights of glory, or to be more precise, one night. I'm talking about that summer evening in July 1990, when I was the warm-up act for one of the world's greatest singers, Frank Sinatra. It was during Glasgow's European City of Culture celebrations. You don't stage Frankie Boy in any old ordinary venue, Jimmy. Oh, no. It was held in the open air before ten thousand 'Swinging Lovers' at Ibrox Park, the home of Rangers Football Club.

So there I was, Jimmy, pacing up and down the dressing-
room before the gig, as you do, and I hear this knock on the door. You can tell a lot by a knock, you know. This one said, Look, I know you're very busy, Arnold, but there's something really important I need to see you about. It turned out to be Frank himself.

He was very apologetic. 'Hey, Arnie, I sure am sorry about this, Buddy, but do you think you could spare me a minute or two of your time?'

I'm a generous person. I could see he looked worried. I couldn't turn him away. I'm not that kind of guy.

'Come on in, Frank. Sit down, make yourself at home. Remember, we're all Jock Tamson's bairns.' I could see from the blank expression on his face he had no idea what I was talking about. All I was trying to do was reassure him that it was no bother at all because when it comes down to it, we're all part of the human race.

He was obviously tense, so I poured him a stiff Jack Daniel's. On the rocks, of course. That seemed to relax him a bit and he began to outline the problem. 'Arnie, I haven't sung in Scotland for years. Being a professional, I always like to talk with the folks in every town I'm playing. Find out what the scene is. What's in the air. Who's who on the streets. That way I can sock it to them, knowing that I've understood what's going on. I really need to know, for example, what my opening song should be. Something that will grab everyone right away, absolutely knock their heads off. People tell me that if there's one person who has got a finger on the pulse of what's happening in Scotland today, it's you, Arnie.'

I leaned back and as I sipped my Highland Spring water, I gave him a run-down on the *Zeitgeist*. I'm a *Zeitgeist* kind of guy. 'Frank, the Scottish people are seething, seething, *seething* . . . They didn't vote for this government and they are aware that the Tories don't give a damn about north of the border. They're quite happy making Scotland the nuclear waste dumping ground of Europe. And they're also quite happy experimenting on the Scots with their Poll Tax, one year earlier than the rest of the UK. Not to mention the pertinent fact, Frank, that they are privatising all our natural assets, such as water and electricity.'

Frank helped himself to another Jack Daniel's and as he savoured it, he said meaningfully: 'The message is coming through loud and clear, Arnie. You're a proud nation suffering under the yoke of the English oppressor. You want independence!' The man obviously had political acumen.

'Yes, Frank, you have summed up the situation perfectly. And in order to articulate the hopes and dreams of the Scottish people, I recommend that your opening song should be "Fly me to Dunoon".'

He loved the idea and left the dressing-room all smiles.

Later, I began to psyche myself up for my performance, the biggest of my career so far. Frank Sinatra. Ten thousand people. Ibrox Park. Glasgow, European City of Culture. It would all look great on the CV . . . Before I knew it, I was on stage. There was a subdued ripple of clapping from the crowd when I appeared. That didn't worry me. Frankly, I don't like too much applause at the start. That's how fascism began.

Of course, I did my 'Growing Up in Glasgow' material and there were quite a few laughs here and there, but being realistic, I understood that they'd all come to see Ol' Blue Eyes and not me. It's a tough scene, this show business, Jimmy.

Naturally, Uncle Harry was there in the front row, **93** cheering me on and I noticed he was wearing a T-shirt with the message 'He's my nephew' on it. I did about fifteen minutes and went off to polite applause. I was not displeased. I had warmed up the evening for the maestro. I did it my way.

Suddenly Sinatra appeared on stage and the whole stadium erupted. He started to sing.

> Fly me to Dunoon,
> And let me play among the stars.

It went down a storm. After that he could do no wrong. He sat down on the edge of the stage, they applauded. He punched the air with his fist, they applauded. He wiped the perspiration from his brow, they applauded. When he did 'Chicago, my kind of town', the reception was ecstatic. He did encore after encore. They just wouldn't let him go.

Afterwards in the hospitality area, everyone crowded round him. 'You're a superstar, Frank.' 'Frankie, you were magic.' 'We all love you, Frank.' Uncle Harry came around with his autograph book, but the minders had already hustled the great man away to a waiting helicopter. Of course, Harry was inconsolable, but by then I wasn't feeling that great myself. No one had said anything to me about how the act had gone. All the attention had been on you know who. I reflected that while I was on, Frank must have been listening while he waited in the wings. But he didn't bother to give me any feedback.

I felt very sorry for myself as I walked back to the Central Hotel, where I was staying. Talk about being out in the cold, Jimmy. You'd think he would have at least said *something*. It would have made my day, or even my year. After all, Frank is a living legend. He's rubbed shoulders with the Kennedys, the Johnsons, the Nixons, the Reagans, the Pope, Mickey Mouse. Admittedly there have been rumours, only rumours mind you, of his association in the past with the Mafia. It was hinted at in that film, *The Godfather*. But be that as it may, there's no denying the man is one of the greatest artists of the twentieth century. And very annoyingly, he hadn't given me any clue at all as to what he thought of my act.

As I climbed into bed, I bumped into something hard and clammy between the sheets. 'What in hell's name is going on,' I thought. 'This is spooky.' In trepidation, I turned on the light and threw back the bedclothes.

It was a horse's head.

22 Susanna MacLeod

Life's strange, Jimmy. One minute you're lying in the gutter having been knocked down by a Rolls-Royce and the next you're snugly ensconced in a four-poster bed. The room

was luxurious, but the décor was oppressive. Everything in view was co-ordinated in salmon pink. Walls, ceiling, carpets, curtains, chest of drawers, clothes cupboard, even the TV set. To the right was a salmon pink door, which presumably led to a salmon pink bathroom. This was penthouse living. The class war is always with us, Jimmy. Around the walls were old prints depicting salmon swimming, salmon entwined in fishing nets and salmon lying supine on dinner plates. I looked down and realised to my horror I was wearing salmon pink pyjamas. I guessed that Malkie must have brought me here. But where was I? I was about to get up and look out the window to get my bearings when the door opened and a nurse walked in. Mercifully she was dressed in white.

'Welcome to the Inhumana Hospital, Mr Brown. You were kept in here last night for observation. All the X-rays revealed that you suffered no more than slight concussion after the Rolls-Royce knocked you down in Sauchiehall Street. To be honest, I was going to say that you slept like a log, but I'm not sure that kind of plebeian simile is appropriate within the prestigious portals of Scotland's leading private hospital. Standards have to be preserved for the privileged few. Can I rephrase that, Mr Brown, if I may? You slept like a seraph in your own blissful, unconscious world, untrammelled by the intrusions of nocturnal clouds of darkness, fear and uncertainty. May I introduce myself. I'm the matron here, Susanna MacLeod.'

'Tell me, matron. I suppose it was Malkie MacDonald who arranged for me to come here. It was his Rolls-Royce that knocked me down.'

'Yes Mr Brown, it *was* Mr MacDonald. He asked me to pass on his best wishes when he phoned early this morning to enquire after your progress. He regrets he was unable to

visit you, but he's had to fly off to Bucharest. He left you
a note.'

Dear Arnold. Hope you are comfortable in the Inhumana. I understand you have no serious injuries.
That's great. You'll be glad to hear that the dent you
caused won't break the bank. I'm off to Romania. Just
landed an order to flood the entire country with ten
million high-tar cigarettes which were proving awfully
difficult to offload in the West. Best wishes for the future.
Malkie.
PS. I still remember all the words of 'The Red Flag'.
Do you?

Matron MacLeod sat down by the bedside: 'Yes, Mr
MacDonald is one of our most esteemed patrons here at
the Inhumana, Mr Brown. You're the twentieth person his
Rolls-Royce has knocked down this year. That generates
a lot of business for us. Now. Doctor Maxwell says that
you can go home any time you choose to after breakfast.
As long as you vacate the room by midday. I can particularly recommend the poached salmon. Mr MacDonald's
chauffeur is waiting in Reception whenever you're ready.
During breakfast, you can read the salmon pink *Financial
Times* and watch TV on ten channels or listen on the
headphones to a CD. I instinctively feel, Mr Brown, you
are a highly sensitive soul. Perhaps Nigel Kennedy's
version of the Brahms Violin Concerto would be just the
very thing to prepare you to face the rigours of the outside world once again. And don't forget, on your bedside
table there's a hotline to the Glasgow Stock Exchange, so
you can be in at the start on the latest privatisation issue.
Oh yes, Mr Brown, here at the Inhumana we also cater for
the *emotional* needs of our valued clientele.'

The soothing sounds of violins cascaded through the
suite. As I tucked into the finest that Tayside could spawn,
the questions ricocheted around in my brain. Why was
Rabbi Freedman behaving in such a strange way? Where
was he hiding at the moment? And above all, why was
Nigel Kennedy's name twice as large on the CD cover as
Brahms's?

Later, as I bathed in the massive circular bath, I turned
on the radio: 'We apologise to listeners who have just
been listening to Rabbi Maurice Freedman on *Thought
for the Day*, in his talk entitled "The Mystic Maze and
the Kabbalah". We regret that this broadcast was an exact
replica of a talk given by Rabbi Lionel Blue yesterday.
This was due to a technical error, for which we apologise.
We are indeed indebted to those listeners who have just
inundated our switchboards to point out this unfortunate
duplication. We also apologise to Rabbi Lionel Blue for
any distress caused by this broadcast and have, of course,
stopped the cheque to Rabbi Freedman.'

So Maurice was still up to his old tricks . . .

It was time to go. I thanked Matron MacLeod and she
photographed me outside the entrance to the hospital. As
we said goodbye to each other, she pressed a polaroid
photograph into my hand and with great passion in her
voice told me: 'This photograph is a permanent testament
to the marvels of private medicine. And remember, Mr
Brown, if you ever need emergency keyhole surgery you
know where to come.'

I climbed into Malkie's Rolls-Royce which was waiting to take me home. Just as we were moving off, a
man rushed up to the window and shouted: 'Can you
spare a kidney, Jimmy?' I completely ignored him. It's
an Inhumana society, I thought to myself. As we purred

along, my thoughts turned to the last time I had been to
see my own doctor for a check-up. I was in the waiting-
room and decided to pass the time finishing a novel. But
after a bit the other patients started complaining about the
noise of the typewriter. The role of the artist in our society
is always a beleaguered one.

When I finally got into the surgery, the doctor wasn't
doing anything medical. He was actually listening to a
Rolf Harris CD. Well, someone's got to do it. When he
saw me coming in, he switched off his headphones and
started listening to my heart. He pointed out that I had a
very commercial beat and recommended me to make an
album.

Then he said he had some terrible news for me. 'Mr
Brown, there's just been a plane crash in Miami. One
hundred and thirty-seven people were killed outright.'

'What's that got to do with me, doctor?' I asked.

'How can you be so callous?' he said contemptuously.

I plucked up courage and asked him if he would
give me a diagnosis of my condition.

'I'm sorry, Mr Brown. I'm afraid you've only got forty
years to live.'

'That's terrible, doctor. Can I have a second opinion?'

'Well, it could be sixty years, if you become a private
patient.'

Medical matters have always been an obsession in our family. Everyone knew that Uncle Harry had been a hypochondriac all his life. It began at the age of thirteen when an elderly aunt gave him a year's subscription to *The Lancet* as a barmitzvah present. Apparently she thought this would plant in his mind the idea of becoming a doctor when he grew up, but it all backfired. Ever since that time, Harry would wake up each morning and begin to scrutinise every inch of his entire body for any spots, swellings or lumps. If he couldn't see a certain area clearly, he used imaginatively placed mirrors. He used to call it 'working late at the orifice'. For many years, this somewhat obsessive behaviour was confined to the privacy of his own flat. Until, that is, one evening in 1953 when he was arrested for a breach of the peace at Central Station during the rush hour.

23　Number thirty-two

The Rolls-Royce ran me smugly all the way back to Calder Street. I felt relaxed after my short stay at the Inhumana, but that all changed when I discovered the door of the flat had been forced open. At a first glance inside, there was nothing to show that there had been an intruder. Then I noticed some bricks had been dismantled in the fireplace. You can't call in the polis just for that, Jimmy.

The phone rang. It was Sam Levine. I decided to skip mentioning the Rolls-Royce and the Inhumana escapades. There were more urgent matters on the agenda. I told him about the break-in and Freedman's *Thought for the Day* fiasco. Sam was unfazed by the news.

'Arnold, all this doesn't surprise me in the least. I've been expecting Freedman to show his hand any day now. Since we last spoke, a few pertinent facts have started to emerge. I realised I had a few pieces in the jigsaw puzzle to piece together. First of all, there was that winning bingo card Harry asked to be buried with in the grave. And the fact that the card contained the number thirty-two, which was encircled presumably because of its Kabbalah significance. And of course, there was that "Clickety-click,

Freedman's sick" telephone message from the Irish woman. It all got me thinking. On a hunch I started to phone all the bingo halls in Glasgow and the suburbs, in every case asking certain leading questions. I came up against a complete blank wall, until strangely enough, my *thirty-second* call to a bingo hall in Castlemilk, which would you believe, happened to have the address, number *thirty-two* Castlemilk Parade, away out in the housing schemes.'

'But what exactly did you find out, Sam?'

'The manager there remembered Harry as a regular. And would you believe this, Arnold? Harry was a big prize winner every time his card had the number thirty-two on it! And when Harry stopped coming, who do you think started to take over the very same table Harry always played at and also went on to win everytime *his* card had the number *thirty-two* on it?'

'Surprise me, Sam?'

'As you've no doubt guessed, Rabbi Maurice Freedman.'

'But Sam, surely a rabbi would never stoop to the degradation of playing bingo in public for prize money. Unless of course, he happened to be in severe financial straits.'

'Arnold, you've hit the nail on the head. Freedman is up to his yarmulka in debt.'

'But why? Presumably rabbis get generous salaries and they're not known for their extravagant life styles.'

'I've got news for you. Rabbi Maurice Freedman is a registered addict!'

'My God, Sam, are you serious? What is it? Heroin, cocaine, crack?'

'No, Arnold, it's more addictive than any of those. Freedman is a smoked salmon addict. He even takes it intravenously.'

'You must be joking. But how did you establish all this?' I asked.

'I can't disclose my sources. Apparently a smoked salmon dealer from Tayside has been coming to Freedman's house in Pollokshields every Friday morning at ten for the last six months.'

'But how did this addiction start?'

'It's an occupational hazard if you're a rabbi. Just think of how many weddings, barmitzvahs and charity events they have to attend. There's a continuous supply of the delicacy thrown at you everywhere. And all for free, of course . . . That's a hell of a lot of temptation.'

'This is a bit of an unusual case, isn't it, Sam?'

'It's not common, I grant you, but Interpol tell me there have been recent cases in Jerusalem, New Jersey and Golders Green.'

'But Sam, where does all this lead us?'

'As I've been speaking, I've been thinking it through. There was something you said. You told me about that talk Freedman stole from Rabbi Lionel Blue. The Kabbalah seems to figure a lot in this case. *That* could be the way forward. There's a place at the Barras market I've heard of. It sells secondhand books and paraphernalia connected with the psychic world. Let's meet there tomorrow morning at eleven. Ask for the stall called "The Mystic Maze".'

24 Fish and chips

When I woke up next morning and thought about going to the Barras market, I instinctively felt that Sam Levine was on the right track. This Kabbalah trail was obviously going to be full of esoteric twists and turns. But that's the nature of the beast, Jimmy.

It was a sunny morning, so I decided to walk there, taking a detour down Allison Street. The scene, as it happened, of one of Harry's most vivid reminiscences.

'When my father, may he rest in peace, died on the 14th April 1948, my sister Sophie and I had to decide whether to carry on the business he had established at 78 Crown Street in 1908. We discussed the matter endlessly for weeks, but we were still undecided as to what to do. Around this time, I was in the middle of reading a treatise by Sigmund Freud, based on a collaboration with Carl Gustav Jung, entitled *The Significance of Number Dreams*. There were so many fascinating topics covered: "Five Hundred Lost Umbrellas and Historical Symbolism in Western Society". "Eighteen Turnips and the Collective Unconscious". "Seven Hundred and Fifty Head Lice and the Vanishing Self". Then a strange thing happened. One evening, I dreamed that I walked into

The Unique fish and chip restaurant in Allison Street. And would you believe it? Freud and Jung were tucking into fish-suppers at one of the tables near the window. They asked me to join them and it turned out they were giving a series of lectures at Glasgow University. The Professor of Psychiatry there had recommended The Unique as having the finest fish and chips in the country.

'The conversation started to get animated and for some reason, maybe because it was all a dream, I didn't feel in the least overawed by being in the presence of two such great minds. In fact, I took the opportunity to point out to them the superiority of the "inner life" over the "outer life". As I explained, when you concentrate on the "inner life", you tend not to go out that much and you save a lot on fares and shoe-leather. Jung remarked that I seemed to be living in cloud-cuckoo land. I retorted quickly that I was very pleased to do this, because that's where the rents are the cheapest.

'Freud turned the conversation to the subject of sex. I mentioned that I had recently cancelled my subscription to *Wild Life* magazine. I told them that I had done this because I objected to reading about insects, who have a better sex life than me. It was a very stimulating discussion and we were all getting on like a house on fire.

'I remarked that we were all Jock Tamson's Bairns, but unfortunately neither Freud nor Jung knew what I was on about. Suddenly a very violent argument broke out. Freud was insisting that it was he who had originally conceived the Theory of Synchronicity. But Jung took great offence at this and was emphatic that he alone should take the credit for it. They almost came to blows, but I managed to save the day.

'"Gentlemen, gentlemen, remember where you are.

This is The Unique, the world-famous fish and chip restaurant. Have you no sense of decorum?" That seemed to quieten both of them down, so I continued. "I think I have a solution to your disagreement. The truth of the matter is that almost certainly both of you conceived The Theory of Synchronicity at *exactly the same time.*"

'They immediately agreed with my sentiments, signed my autograph book and paid the bill. For some reason, Freud asked for an orange at the counter but there were none available. They then quietly left the premises, much to the relief of my friend Mr Jaconelli, the proprietor, who had been on the verge of dialling 999.'

25   The changeover

The next day, I quizzed Harry further about the changeover in the family business. He continued his story.

'The morning after my Freud and Jung dream, I woke up thinking about fruit. Freud's request for an orange had jogged my memory and I recalled that was the fruit my angel, David, had given me as a present at our first meeting in the summer of 1947.

'After breakfast, I was walking in Victoria Road, Arnold, when all of a sudden, complete strangers began to call out to me from the other side of the street. One man shouted out that he was going off to practise with the Flute Band in preparation for the coming Orange Walk. Another man advised me to bet on a horse running that day called Highland Orange. And the third stranger asked me if "I was contemplating my navel". All these references to oranges . . . It was bewildering. Surely it must all mean something, I thought. Some sort of message.

'It got me thinking how wonderful fruit is. Healthy, energy-giving, full of all the vitamins. A gift from nature and a blessing. Surely something as special as fruit should be available to everyone, rich and poor alike. Suddenly

I had a vision. Pears in Polmadie. Grapes in Govanhill. Pomegranates in Possil. Melons in Maryhill. Apples in Anderston. Peaches in Parkhead. Glasgow, a Garden of Eden for the working people. All the signs were clearly telling me to convert the family tailor shop into a fruit shop!

'I rushed over to see my sister, Sophie, and she was as enthusiastic as I was. I even devised a great slogan for the opening window display which would embody the sanctity of fruit. "Don't squeeze me till I'm yours."

'In this inspired mood, Arnold, nothing can stop me. I then had the idea to write to the Minister of Health pointing out that in the films the stars all smoked like chimneys. What sort of example is that to the younger generation, I asked? I begged the Minister to ask Hollywood to put an end to this outrageous behaviour. I said I envisaged the day in the not so distant future when someone like Humphrey Bogart would give up smoking on the screen and, instead, be happy to be seen munching on the occasional Granny Smith. The odd thing is, I never received a reply to that letter.'

26   Merchant City

I was still on my way to The Mystic Maze. I passed through Candleriggs, the location of the old Fruit Market. Here, west of the High Street, was 'Merchant City', where the Tobacco Lords built their magnificent mansions and made Glasgow the most important tobacco-trading city in Europe by the middle of the eighteenth century. And yes, Jimmy, it could be said they can also take the credit for Glasgow being one of the lung cancer capitals of the

world by the middle of the twentieth century. Nowadays, the area has been reclaimed by the professional classes and their influence is everywhere. As I was passing a butcher's shop, I noticed its unusual name: 'Sirloins'. I stepped inside to check it out. There was the usual carnage on display, but this was a different kind of butcher's shop. Rock music blared out from huge speakers hanging from the ceiling and strobe lights dazzled the customers milling around the counters. A waitress in a black leather mini-skirt approached me.

'Welcome to Sirloins, sir. I'm Morag. Can I offer you one of our exquisite cocktails while you're waiting?'

'No thanks, I'm in a hurry. Just tell me, please, is this a butcher's shop?'

Morag laughed. 'Och no, sir. You're a bit out of touch. We *used* to be a butcher's shop, but we felt that Merchant City was in need of something a little more recherché, if you know what I mean, sir.'

To be honest, I didn't. 'Sorry?'

'Well sir, we are now meat stylists.'

'What on earth is that?'

'We match the meat to your personality. It's the latest thing from San Francisco, sir.' Morag ushered me into one of the curtained-off kiosks where, she explained, a trained counsellor would go through a series of tests with me to ensure 'complete carnal compatability'. Fifteen minutes later, I walked out with a pound of pigs' trotters . . .

By now I was feeling slightly overwrought. I was tempted to pop into The Body Shop, but a glance at their window with its garish posters promoting Hazel-Nut Buttock Balm from the Amazon made me hurry on. Next door, a red and yellow lion rampant Scottish flag was draped across the Caledonia Wholefoods shop. I saw with satisfaction the notice in the window: 'Highland Health Foods. Guaranteed untouched by English hands.'

As I was passing The Riveters' Wine Bar, a man came up to me. 'Hey Jimmy. There's a few things that have been bothering me recently. Do you think you can help me out?'

'Fire away. I'll help if I can,' I replied.

'Thanks, son. First of all, I've noticed a lot of punters are starting to wear yon baseball caps back to front. For God's sake, tell us why they're doing that?'

I sensed he needed calming down and I was happy to be the one to do it.

'I think I've got the answer for you. They obviously think they're being followed. They're trying to shake off their pursuers. It's simply paranoia.'

'That's dead brilliant, Jimmy. You're a wee genius, so you are. Next question. Tell me, son. Why is it all the tabloids have got astrological forecasts, but there's none at all in any of the posh papers?'

'That's an easy one,' I assured him. I was getting into my stride. 'In our society, perhaps the chattering classes have got no future.'

'Och, Jimmy. Your intellect is sheer magic. Now, here's one last question. Why do fools fall in love?'

I racked my brains for a few minutes, but I still couldn't come up with the goods. This was a real teaser.

'Sorry, you've got me there. I don't think I can help you with that one. But I know a certain alleyway off Sauchiehall Street that can . . .'

27 The Mystic Maze

I had now reached the Barras market, which is in the Gallowgate, just west of Glasgow Cross in the east end of the city. To find The Mystic Maze was not that easy, for there's a square mile of markets, stalls and barrows to search through. When I asked a stall-holder, he gave me the exact directions and a bit of philosophy thrown in. 'Och, a' that stuff about the paranormal fair gives me the creeps, so it does. Mind ye, if ah want to be real feart, ah jist turn on the telly and watch some Tory go oan aboot yon Nicholas Fairbairn bein' the next Prime Minister.'

Eventually I found The Mystic Maze inside the covered section of the market. It was much bigger than I had expected. On the ground floor, thousands of books on the paranormal and the occult were stacked around in no apparent order, as if they had just mysteriously material-ised. There was a sign pointing to the floors upstairs:

CONSULTING ROOMS
PSYCHICS/MEDIUMS/HEALERS/COUNSELLORS

There's a hell of a lot of lost people out there, Jimmy . . .

On the wall, a noticeboard leaflet advised visitors to the

city that one of the special attractions was 'The Alleyway of a Thousand Questions'. 'Problems solved while you walk. Enlightenment and exercise in one unforgettable experience.' I was proud that Harry's brainchild had been recommended by the Glasgow Tourist Board.

Sam Levine was nowhere to be seen and I was trying to work out what to do when an old man in a fez and a silk smoking-jacket came over to me: 'By the description

Mr Levine gave me, you must be Arnold Brown. You've
just missed him by a few minutes. Mr Levine regrets he
cannot be here to meet you as arranged, but he's given
me this letter for you, which he says will explain everything.
By the way, I'm Meldrum Forsyth. I specialise in talismans,
individually crafted to your needs. Just the thing to clear
your inner life of negative energies. And remember, we
do take Access and Visa.' I declined his kind offer and
tore open Sam's letter.

Dear Arnold

 Arrived a bit early for our meeting. Atmosphere of Mystic
Maze overwhelming. Consulted psychic medium.
Adamant that I had to stop chasing 'religious gentleman
with beard'. Claimed she had a seance with him just five
minutes earlier. She'd sent him off to 32 Westmoreland
Street in Crosshill. Afraid must drop Freedman case.
Psychic says I'll be the one to solve mystery of the corn-
circles. Off to Wiltshire. Sorry to leave you in lurch.

 Yours,
 Sam

I was a bit taken aback by Sam's defection, but as
we all know, in the recession you've got to go where
the work is. But that wasn't the most surprising aspect
of the letter. I ran out into the Gallowgate and hailed a
taxi. '32 Westmoreland Street and step on it,' I said to
the driver. The taxi screeched through the back streets
towards the South Side and soon we had zoomed past
Eglinton Toll, down Victoria Road and reached number
32 Westmoreland Street in record time. The address was
more than a little familiar to me. It was the home of my
shy and retiring relative, Auntie Sophie . . .

28 32 Westmoreland Street

I looked up at Auntie Sophie's window. The glass was covered in soap suds and more were being flung at the pane from the inside. I assumed she was cleaning her rent book as usual. To be honest, she has always had a thing about cleanliness and is constantly washing her hands. Occasionally in the past she had taken in lodgers, but they never stayed more than a few nights because Sophie always insisted on washing their hands too.

My ninety-year-old relative was not the only one obsessed with cleanliness. Her once grimy tenement now sported the new Glasgow Corporation colour, beige. The City Fathers had decided to sandblast all the old stone Victorian buildings. That was such a popular success that the council allocated an annual budget of several million pounds to sandblast clean the faces of the city's Senior Citizens.

I rang the bell and Auntie Sophie came to the door. Life is so predictable, Jimmy. She was soaked from head to foot.

'Auntie Sophie, you're all wet.'

'Arnold son, ah would be. Ahm bathing the budgie.'

I stepped inside. In the far corner near the TV set was

a large cloud of soap suds. I could just make out the bars
of a budgie's cage. The front room was full of washing-up
liquids and detergent bottles. The budgie, now dried and
safely back in its cage, was looking as clean as the outside
of the tenement. I decided not to plunge in right away with
leading questions about visits from religious gentlemen with
beards. Auntie Sophie was sometimes a bit cantankerous
and first of all I had to judge her mood.

'Well, Auntie Sophie, how are you keeping?'

'Och, pretty good, considering.'

'Considering what?'

'Considering now that ahm ninety, there's no much
chance of me ever being a TV news announcer.'

'Life begins at ninety, Auntie Sophie,' I said.

Looking more and more harassed, Auntie Sophie started
to scurry around the room in search of something. She
eventually found what she was looking for in the pocket
of her apron.

'Och, it was right here all the time. That Alzheimer has got a lot to answer for, ah can tell you.' She pulled out a long brass telescope and went over to the window and looked through the old instrument at the tenement opposite.

'What's up?' I asked.

'Shh!' She continued to look through the telescope. 'Ah've just joined the Neighbourhood Watch Scheme.'

The telescope quivered. Auntie Sophie had seen something which made her very angry indeed.

'Ma God. That hoity-toity Mrs Johnstone has got a new colour telly. Bugger it. It's *twice* as big as mine.'

'I sympathise. It's a cruel world, Auntie Sophie.'

'Aye, it sure is, son. You know, ah can remember when we all had a sing-song round the old piano. Now these wee Japs, they've got everyone hooked on yon karaoke. Not only that, the whole world is against us Senior Citizens.'

'Auntie Sophie! You, a Senior Citizen? You look great after all that sandblasting.'

'Flattery will get you nowhere, Arnold. The truth is that we OAPs are treated like dirt. For instance, look at these street signs all over the place.'

'You've lost me, Auntie. What do you mean?'

'You know the signs ahm talking about. They're everywhere. "Beware Elderly Persons Crossing." If that's no
prejudice, hen, ah don't know what is.'

I felt it was time to move things along a little.

'By the way, Auntie Sophie, has Rabbi Maurice Freedman been here to see you today?'

'Aye, son, you just missed him.'

'What did he want to see you about?'

'Ah couldnae make head or tail of what he was on
about. First of all, he chaps that loudly on the door, ah
thought it was the polis. Ah let him in and the first thing he
says to me is that he'd love a smoked salmon sandwich. Ah
couldnae believe ma ears. How did he expect a pensioner
like me to have a luxury like that in the house. You should
have seen his face fall when I told him he was out of luck.
Then he started to ask questions about Harry.'

'What sort of questions, Auntie Sophie?'

'He asked me if Harry had left anything behind with
me before he died.'

'And did he, Auntie Sophie?'

'Aye, he left two things – a launderette ticket and the
key to a locker at the Left Luggage in Central Station.'

I suddenly remembered the message Harry had left
for me in his flat . . . 'We are all left luggage waiting to
be collected.' I began to feel as if things were falling into
place.

'And did you give him the launderette ticket and the
key?'

'Ah gave him – ' She interrupted herself and rushed
over to a small chest of drawers. 'Before ah forget, Arnold,
dae you like these?'

Sophie held up a spotlessly clean football jersey for
me to inspect. 'Ahm in goal. This afternoon it's the final

of the Senior Citizens' John MacLean Memorial Cup.'

'Auntie Sophie, you were about to tell me more about your conversation with the rabbi.'

'Och, aye. So I was, son. Now, what happened? Aye. Now ah remember. Ah didnae like the way he'd barged in on me demanding smoked salmon, so ah just gave him the launderette ticket and held on tae the key of the locker.'

I had a good laugh to myself at the thought of Maurice feverishly scrabbling through Harry's washing in the search for something of significance. I told Sophie I'd collect the left luggage and as she handed over the key, she told me something else.

'Oh, Arnold, there was one more thing. Rabbi Freedman was in such a rush to go that he dropped this envelope. You might as well have it, hen. Ah've no idea what it all means.'

I recognised right away the gold-framed Hebrew inscription from Harry's flat. Stapled below, there was a typed translation in English on Rabbi Freedman's personal writing paper.

When I met God in the Princes Square Shopping Mall in January 1991, he signed my autograph book. At the same time he dedicated a message to me.

(Sgd) Harry Brown

'I'll keep this, Auntie Sophie. I'm off now. Best of luck with the match.'

'Nae bother at all, Arnold. With all the training ah've done this season, ah've just hit peak form.'

29 Timing

Here we go again . . . I stopped a taxi in Victoria Road and we rattled along towards Central Station. In the back seat, I pondered on the fact that I had just missed confronting Rabbi Maurice Freedman by only a few minutes. Timing: the essence of all activities . . . And that was the same conclusion Harry had come to in the late 1980s. He told me that for many years he had been grappling with Einstein's Theory of Relativity and as a result of this intellectual effort, he became obsessed with the whole concept of time and timing. As a professional comedian, I identify with this a lot, Jimmy. In my view, the most important thing about comedy is timing. For example, the audience go to the theatre on a certain night and I arrive a week later – that's bad timing. I'm a hardened professional. I've noticed it makes a difference even one day out.

It gradually occurred to Harry that perhaps he himself was capable of making a literary contribution to the subject. (He had been encouraged in 1979 when he had spent two weeks in Dunoon finishing his first letter to *The Times*, which to his great delight was published. The letter was part of his campaign to persuade supermarkets and department stores to have grandfather clocks instead of ordinary ones.) As usual, Harry's interest in a subject turned into an ongoing obsession and he spent months researching time and all its various dimensions. He struggled to find his own individual approach to the subject. Then one day he told me he had decided on a title. *A Brief History of Timekeeping.* It was to be based on the stories and reminiscences of Glasgow's shipyard workers. I remember Harry's words. 'Arnold, everything in life depends on whether an action is a split-second too early or too late. No matter what it is, whether it's clocking into a shipyard, a factory or an office, or running for a bus, or even God's creation of the world, the crucial factor is timing.'

Harry filled his notebooks with all the exciting stories from the veterans who had clocked in, day in day out,

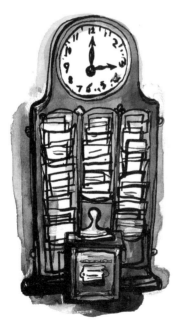

at John Brown's shipyard. They were the ones who had built the great ships, the *Queen Mary* and the two *Queen Elizabeths*, to such tight deadlines. Eventually he had a manuscript which he sent off to countless publishers, all of whom rejected it. He was forced to publish it himself privately and managed to get a small bookshop in Victoria Road to stage a booksigning. Sadly, Harry slept in that morning. And so did the printer who was supposed to deliver the books to the shop. And of course, when Stephen Hawking's *A Brief History of Time* came out a few months later to ecstatic reviews, Harry was heartbroken. If only he hadn't included the word 'keeping' in his own title.

30 Central Station

The taxi stopped outside the rank at Central Station, yards away from the entrance to the Central Hotel. Here, on the morning of 15th August 1925, Albert Einstein, like Harry, had been particularly exercised by the concept of time. As soon as he woke up, Einstein rang down to reception to check if he was too late for breakfast.

The locker number was thirty-two. Surprise, surprise. I turned the key and the door swung open to reveal an old white plastic carrier-bag. Inside was a battered-looking leatherbound autograph book. I decided to complete my detective work in the Refreshments Bar over a pot of Earl Grey. As I sipped my tea, I flicked through all the signatures. The book was packed with the names of world statesmen, political activists, sporting personalities and 'stars of stage, screen and radio'. No name was less than legendary and that included Enrico Lombardi, the Glasgow ice-cream king. But on the very last page was the most bizarre signature of all, together with a message.

Dear Harry
When you are confused by life's problems, go to the Gents' Department at any branch of Marks and Spencer. There you will find a small sign:
'If in doubt, ask to be measured'.
God

31 The verdict

Our ref: AB/3221

Sotheby's
34 New Bond Street
London W1 2AK

5th April 1994

Arnold Brown Esq
12 Hampstead Gardens
London NW3 1TT

Dear Mr Brown

RE: AUTOGRAPH BOOK OF HARRY BROWN

We thank you for your enclosure of 22nd March last,
and have examined with interest the above document. We
wish to advise you that we are of the opinion that none of
the signatures contained therein can be authenticated with
the exception of the one signed by 'God'.

Your esteemed instructions are awaited.

Yours faithfully,

Richard Wells, Graphology Department

Epilogue

If there's anything in this book you haven't understood, please regard it as significant.